FOUR-STAR PLAYS
for BOYS

☆　　☆　　☆　　☆

Four-Star Plays
for Boys

*A collection of fifteen royalty-free, one-act plays
for all-boy casts*

Edited by

A. S. Burack

Publishers　　　　PLAYS, INC.　　　　*Boston*

Contents

Junior and Senior High

Middle Grades

Lower Grades

FOUR-STAR PLAYS
for BOYS

Final Edition

by George Wallace Sayre

Characters

TAYLOR ⎫
PHILLIPS ⎬ *reporters*
RICHARDS ⎪
BLONDY ⎭
JIMMY, *copy boy*
ROBERT WELCH, *managing editor*
HANK POWELL, *city editor*
ALDERMAN SIMPSON

SCENE 1

SETTING: *The editorial room of a metropolitan newspaper. There are five battered desks around the room which are covered with copy paper, clippings and newspapers.*

AT RISE: *The click of the typewriters and the teletype machine continues monotonously. The large desk of* HANK POWELL, *which is situated in the foreground, is empty. Three reporters,* TAYLOR, PHILLIPS *and* RICHARDS, *are busy working.* TAYLOR'S *voice rises above the noise of the room as he yells for the copy boy.*

TAYLOR: Copy! (*He picks up several sheets of paper from*

3

his desk, sorts them, and yanks the sheet from his type-writer. Then again, more insistently, he bawls out) Jimmy! Copy! Will somebody tell me where that boy hides? (*The telephone on* POWELL'S *desk starts to ring.*)

PHILLIPS: Will somebody answer that phone?

RICHARDS: Ten to one it's ants-in-the-pants again.

PHILLIPS: Tell him to fry an egg.

RICHARDS (*He gets up wearily and crosses to the desk.*): Only one egg? (*Entering through the swinging doors at left,* JIMMY *comes breezily into the room.*)

JIMMY (*Innocently*): Somebody call?

TAYLOR: Over here! Where in blazes have you been?

JIMMY: It's a long story, Mr. Taylor. But if you insist . . .

RICHARDS (*As he answers the city editor's phone*): City desk. Yes, Mr. Simpson . . . (*Pause*) Mr. Powell hasn't come in yet . . . (*Pause*) Yes, Mr. Simpson . . . (*Pause*) . . . I'll give him your message the minute he comes in, Mr. Simpson . . . (*He wearily hangs up.*) That was Mr. City Alderman Simpson.

PHILLIPS: Is he still burning?

RICHARDS: You can smell it over the phone.

TAYLOR (*Hands* JIMMY *his copy*): See if you can get this down to the pressroom today.

JIMMY: Yes, sir! Right away, sir! (JIMMY *gives* TAYLOR *a military salute, takes the copy and crosses to the swinging doors.*)

TAYLOR (*Calling after* JIMMY): While you're down there, find out *why* Tony hasn't sent up my lunch.

JIMMY (*Salutes again*): Yes, sir! (JIMMY *exits.* TAYLOR *rises from his desk, stretches his legs, as though cramped from sitting, and crosses to the water cooler.*)

RICHARDS: The tone of Simpson's voice tells me that he's a troubled, unhappy sorehead.

TAYLOR: Just what was the nature of sorehead's complaint?

RICHARDS: He demands that Hank Powell call him at once.

TAYLOR: The nerve of the guy!

PHILLIPS: There's not a bigger crook in town!

TAYLOR: He's a good politician—meets every issue with an open mouth.

RICHARDS: Wonder what our esteemed managing editor is going to say?

PHILLIPS: He'll stand behind Hank. (*The telephone rings on the City Desk.* RICHARDS *answers it again.*)

RICHARDS: City desk! . . . (*Pause*) Will you spell the name, please? (*Starts writing on sheet of paper*) Is that spelled with a *G* as in grapefruit? . . . Oh, pardon *me,* sir . . . *L* as in lemons. Yes, sir. . . . Yes, sir. . . . Thank you, sir. (*Hangs up*) Twins born to Mr. and Mrs. Samuel Larrity, assorted package. Six and a half, and seven pounds, two ounces.

TAYLOR: How is the poor father doing? (RICHARDS *looks at the papers before him on* HANK'S *desk. He holds up a sheet of proof and reads.*)

RICHARDS: Now listen to this! Listen to this! Quote— And these three boats of the Inland Excursions Company, built in 1930, daily take thousands of sightseers, women and children, on trips up the river. Last April, the City Steamship Inspectors condemned the boats of the rival Dickenson Riverboat Company whose boats were built in 1935. Maybe the public would better understand this action if they knew that Alderman Joseph Simpson is the owner of Inland Excursions. Unquote!

TAYLOR: Is that printed?

RICHARDS: Don't you ever read your own sheet? It hit the first edition this morning.

TAYLOR: No wonder Simpson is frothing. If I know Hank, that's only the warm-up. Just wait until he really starts throwing punches.

PHILLIPS: We can use some excitement. (BLONDY, *another reporter, enters through the swinging doors, and goes to the water cooler to pour himself a drink.*)

PHILLIPS: Hi, Blondy.

BLONDY: Hi, slaves. Anything doing around this dump?

TAYLOR: Dull as Tony's coffee.

RICHARDS: Have you seen Hank?

BLONDY: Hasn't he been in yet?

RICHARDS: No word all morning.

BLONDY: I saw him down at the docks about ten o'clock, but he drove away in a hurry before I could speak to him.

RICHARDS: Did you catch the first edition?

BLONDY: Yeah! Maybe we'll have some fireworks. The sheet can use a shot in the arm.

TAYLOR: Hank's got plenty of ammunition this time.

RICHARDS: I'll say he has . . .

BLONDY: If any of you gentlemen are interested, Mr. Robert Welch, our Managing Editor, in person, was driving up in his shiny new car as I came in.

PHILLIPS: How do you like this guy! *Now* he tells us! (BLONDY *grins at the jibes and takes a position by the cooler, pouring another drink of water.* PHILLIPS, TAYLOR *and* RICHARDS *immediately become exceedingly busy at their desks. They are typing furiously as* ROBERT WELCH, *the Managing Editor, enters through the swinging doors. For a moment he surveys the busy scene and his face is serious and thoughtful.*)

WELCH: Good morning, men.

REPORTERS: 'Morning, Mr. Welch. (WELCH *crosses to the center of the room and stops before* HANK's *desk*.)

WELCH: Isn't Hank in yet? (*The men exchange quick glances, and* PHILLIPS *becomes the spokesman for the others*.)

PHILLIPS: He called . . . said he was detained on some business.

WELCH: Tell Hank I want to see him *immediately,* when he comes in.

PHILLIPS: Yes, sir. (WELCH *crosses to the door of his office and exits. The reporters watch him, and when the door closes they exchange significant glances*.)

RICHARDS: What does that mean?

TAYLOR: Fundamental, my dear Richards. Our Managing Editor doesn't like the stories Hank writes.

PHILLIPS: You're nuts!

TAYLOR: May we quote you, Mr. Phillips?

RICHARDS: What about all the advertising Simpson and Inland Excursions throw the paper?

PHILLIPS: Advertising or no advertising, Welch will stand back of Hank.

RICHARDS: I'd hate to see Hank out on a limb.

PHILLIPS: You wise guys will see I'm right.

BLONDY: While you're fighting it out, I'm going to run over to Police Headquarters and see if I can get a human interest yarn. There should be some kid lost.

TAYLOR: A good dog fight would do. (BLONDY *exits briskly.* JIMMY *enters, carrying a sandwich wrapped in paper and a cup of steaming coffee. He crosses to* TAYLOR's *desk*.)

JIMMY: Here's your alleged lunch. (*He places the sandwich and coffee on the desk*.) Tony says no more until you pay up.

TAYLOR: He'll get my personal check . . . *any* Saturday. (*Takes a sip of the coffee and makes a face.*) Hey . . . where's the sugar?

JIMMY: Pardon me . . . I forgot. (*He takes two white "cubes" from his pocket and tosses them adroitly into the cup.* TAYLOR *jumps back to avoid being splashed.*)

TAYLOR: Do that again and Mrs. Sullivan will be missing her charming son!

JIMMY: Gee . . . I'm sorry.

TAYLOR: Get busy and clean up the trash around here.

JIMMY: Yes, sir . . . right away, sir. (JIMMY *walks around the room, picking up the papers and cramming them into the wastebaskets.*)

TAYLOR: I have a suspicion that kid is needling me. (*Takes a bite of the sandwich and a sip of coffee.*) What coffee!

RICHARDS: What about Senator Hamilton? I'm still holding his obituary.

PHILLIPS: Doc Harwood said he's better today.

RICHARDS: How do you like that guy! It knocks out half a column. (TAYLOR *is devouring his sandwich while he talks.*)

TAYLOR: Lay it aside. Maybe he'll croak tomorrow.

RICHARDS: He's sure missing a big opportunity. He could have made the front page by dying today.

PHILLIPS: It's not like the Senator to miss any front-page publicity.

TAYLOR: Let's see if we can knock some copy together. Hank may need it, when he gets in. (*The telephone on the City Desk rings.* RICHARDS *crosses to the desk and answers.*)

PHILLIPS: Ten to one it's Twinkle-toes Simpson.

RICHARDS (*Into phone*): City desk . . . (*Pause*) . . . yes,

Mrs. Twinkle— I mean, Mrs. *Winkle*wood. (*He writes on pad*) . . . I understand, Mrs. Winklewood . . . We'll take care of it, Mrs. Winklewood. (*Hangs up*) That was . . .

PHILLIPS, TAYLOR (*In unison*): Mrs. Winklewood!

RICHARDS: She lost her cat again. Broken-hearted . . .

PHILLIPS: What do you suppose is keeping Hank?

TAYLOR: Maybe he went home for lunch. His boy is on vacation now.

RICHARDS: Anybody ever see Hank's boy?

TAYLOR: I met him at a store one day. Hank was buying him a football outfit—spending dough like a millionaire.

PHILLIPS: What's the boy like?

TAYLOR: As a rule I don't go for kids. Most of them are a lot of ill-bred brats. But this boy—Ronald's his name— is *all* boy. He's polite, respectful and smart. Hank's done a bang-up job of raising him.

RICHARDS (*Innocently*): Didn't Mrs. Powell have anything to do with it?

TAYLOR: Are you trying to be a comedian?

RICHARDS (*Assumed modesty*): It comes naturally. (*The telephone on the City Desk rings.*)

TAYLOR: If I'm not asking too much, will you *please* answer that instrument?

RICHARDS (*Grinning*): My pleasure, sir. (*As* RICHARDS *crosses to the City Desk to answer the phone,* TAYLOR *takes a sip of his coffee. It nearly gags him and he sputters and coughs.*)

TAYLOR: What coffee!

RICHARDS (*Into phone*): City Desk . . . (*Pause*) . . . yes, sir . . . Thank you, sir. (*He hangs up*) A press release from the Governor's Mansion. The Governor's son has had a nervous breakdown from studying too hard.

PHILLIPS: Was it a blonde or brunette? (*TAYLOR has been stirring his coffee with the paper knife and now extracts two marbles, which he holds up.*)

TAYLOR: *Jimmy!*

JIMMY: Yes, sir . . .

TAYLOR (*Burning yet trying to be patient*): In the name of sainted Murphy—are these the two lumps of sugar you put in my coffee?

JIMMY (*Stares with amazement at the marbles*): Gee . . . my marbles. (*TAYLOR grabs the paper knife, slowly rises from his desk and advances at JIMMY menacingly. JIMMY fearfully backs away, while the other reporters watch with amusement.*)

TAYLOR: That does it!

JIMMY: *Please*, Mr. Taylor! Let me explain! (*TAYLOR holds the paper knife menacingly as he continues slowly advancing toward JIMMY, who continues backing toward the doors.*)

TAYLOR: Phillips, here's a scoop for you! At eleven-thirty this morning, Eric Taylor, Assistant City Editor on the *City News,* suddenly attacked the copy boy, Jimmy Sullivan, with a paper knife.

PHILLIPS: Was there a motive?

TAYLOR: Poisoned coffee!

PHILLIPS: Shall I say the victim was stabbed through the heart?

TAYLOR: Throat was cut from ear to ear! (*As JIMMY fearfully backs toward the swinging doors, TAYLOR advances toward him, holding the knife menacingly. Then as the frightened JIMMY is about to turn and run from the room, the swinging doors open and HANK POWELL enters. He hurriedly makes for his desk, talking as he goes.*)

HANK: Gather around men! We have work to do! (TAYLOR, PHILLIPS, RICHARDS *and* JIMMY *immediately gather around* HANK'S *desk.* HANK *slips out of his coat and hangs it on a rack nearby, and then slips into a worn alpaca office coat, talking as he moves. At his desk, he gets busy sorting papers, reading the notes, talking rapidly, enthusiastically, all the while.* JIMMY *watches him adoringly;* TAYLOR, PHILLIPS *and* RICHARDS *listen with the attention which* HANK *commands through sheer personality.*)

HANK: Have you read the first edition?

ALL (*In unison*): Yes, sir.

HANK: Now I've got the facts, and we can lay it on the line! It's the biggest scandal this city has had in years!

TAYLOR: Mr. Welch said he wanted to see you the minute you came in.

HANK: Too busy now! How much time do we have before we close the forms?

TAYLOR: About thirty minutes.

HANK: We'll have to hustle to make it! Have Mack set up a three-column heading: *Obsolete Steamers Operating Excursions!* Here are my notes—blow it up, make up some sub-heads and let me see them!

TAYLOR: Yes, sir. (*He starts away, and then returns.*) Alderman Simpson has been calling all morning. He's sore.

HANK: Let him read about it! Get busy! We haven't any time to waste! (TAYLOR *glances at* RICHARDS *and* PHILLIPS, *shrugs and crosses quickly to his desk, where he starts typing.*) Richards . . . find out the names of the license commissioners, and get their pictures!

RICHARDS: Right away. (RICHARDS *quickly crosses to his desk.*)

HANK: Phillips, I want you to get busy in the morgue and dig up pictures of all the river boats! See if you can find something about river catastrophes . . . we'll use them for a follow-up in the Night Edition!

PHILLIPS: Yes, sir. (PHILLIPS *quickly goes to his desk, grabs up paper and pencils, and exits through the swinging doors. JIMMY, now alone before HANK's desk, watches him admiringly as he busies himself with the copy on his desk. Finally, HANK finishes and hands JIMMY the copy.*)

HANK: Jimmy . . . rush this down to the composing room!

JIMMY: Yes, sir! (JIMMY *hurriedly crosses the room and exits through the swinging doors. HANK busies himself with the copy on his desk. He talks, half to himself, and half to TAYLOR and RICHARDS who are pounding their typewriters at their desks.*)

HANK: When John Q. Public reads this, he'll have his eyes opened to the "slip me" game in city politics—"you slip me and I'll slip you"! By the time I'm finished, we'll have a lot of indignant citizens—some fine heads are going to roll . . . (*The fire signal on the wall rings. HANK, TAYLOR and RICHARDS glance at it as a number flashes up on the signal board.*) Richards . . . get on that fire! Two twenty-six! Probably somebody's ash can, but get the story!

RICHARDS: Yes, sir. Right away! (RICHARDS *gets busy on the phone, to find out the location and nature of the fire.*)

HANK: Taylor . . . how're you doing?

TAYLOR: It's making beautiful copy.

HANK (*Glances at watch*): Keep at it! (HANK's *phone rings and he picks up the receiver.*) Hello . . . City Desk . . . (*A pleased look comes over his face as he listens*) Yes, Blondy . . . that's fine. Keep on it and call me the minute you find out what it is. (HANK *hangs up the receiver and speaks to* TAYLOR *and* RICHARDS.) Blondy's got something. That fire is up around the Park District, near the river. He's getting a ride in a police car . . . (HANK *stops as the doors swing open and* ALDERMAN SIMPSON *enters. He holds a newspaper tightly in his fist. His eyes sweep the room, and seeing* HANK *at his desk, he quickly crosses to him.* TAYLOR *and* RICHARDS *watch* SIMPSON *and exchange significant glances.*)

SIMPSON (*To* HANK): I want to speak to you!

HANK: Well, if it isn't Alderman Simpson! It's been a long time since you honored the *News* with your presence.

SIMPSON (*Angrily*): Who is responsible for printing this outrageous story?

HANK: What story do you mean?

SIMPSON (*Hitting paper*): This! . . . About Inland Excursions! I'll not stand for it! You'll run an immediate retraction!

HANK: There's nothing to get excited about, Alderman. You *are* the president of Inland Excursions, aren't you?

SIMPSON: You know it's my company.

HANK: I just wanted to hear it from your own lips. Put that in your copy, Taylor.

SIMPSON: What are you getting at? This story is libelous!

HANK: Do you really want to know what I'm getting at, Alderman?

SIMPSON: I'll not take your impudence!

HANK: O.K., I'll tell you. I'm going to bust your rotten

operations wide open. Every word in that story is true. I saw the conditions myself.

SIMPSON: What conditions, Powell?

HANK: Glad you asked that. Your company, Inland Excursions, hasn't provided for the safety of passengers, Mr. Alderman. Every day you take hundreds of sightseers, mostly women and children, up the river on rotten tubs you have the nerve to call river boats. They have rotten life-preservers . . . inch-wide seams on the lifeboats . . .

SIMPSON: You're a liar!

HANK: Then sue me—sue the paper, if you can prove the story *is* libelous.

SIMPSON: I'll show you! I'll have you fired! I'll see that you never work in this city again!

HANK: Look, Mr. Simpson . . . who do you think you are, coming around here trying to dictate the policies of this paper? This isn't Russia . . . (*A definite pause*) Thank God we have a free press!

SIMPSON: We'll see about that, you cheap, scandal-mongering hack writer! (SIMPSON *turns abruptly and crosses to the door labeled "Managing Editor" and goes into the office.* HANK *sorts the papers on his desk and starts writing. For a moment there is a dead silence in the room as the men watch him. Then* HANK *becomes aware of his men's stares and looks up angrily.*)

HANK: All right, you guys. This is still a newspaper office and we've got work to do. (*The fire signal on the wall rings again and shocks the men into nervous activity.*) That's the second alarm! (*Looks quickly about his desk*) Where is the telephone book? Somebody get me a telephone book! I never worked in a newspaper office where anybody could find a telephone book—what do you guys use them for? (TAYLOR *crosses to* HANK'S *desk with a telephone book . . . dog-eared and torn . . . but a telephone book.* HANK *grabs it and hastily turns the pages.*) Call the Fire Department and try to find out what's going on.

TAYLOR: Yes, sir. (TAYLOR *crosses to his desk and starts dialing his telephone.* HANK *scans the pages of the telephone book.*)

HANK: This'll do . . . a delicatessen . . . (*Dials number*) Hello . . . Parkside Delicatessen? . . . What do you know about the fire up your way? (*Pause as he listens*) No—this is the *City News* . . . yes . . . *a newspaper!* Will you please look out your window . . . can't you see the smoke? (*Pause*) Smoke . . . (*Spells it*) S-M-O-K-E! Hello . . . Hello . . . (*Disgustedly*) Hung up! Now I've got to get hold of Blondy. He should be up there by this time . . . Jimmy! . . . Jimmy! (JIMMY *enters quickly through the swinging doors and crosses to* HANK's *desk.*)

JIMMY: Yes, Mr. Powell. (HANK *has scribbled on a piece of paper. He hands it to* JIMMY.)

HANK: Take this down to the composing room. Tell Smithy to hold four columns of the first page. (*At his desk,* TAYLOR *hangs up his phone and crosses excitedly to* HANK's *desk.*)

TAYLOR: It's big, Hank! The fire department says the fire is on a boat up the river!

HANK (*Tersely*): A boat! What kind of a boat? What kind of newspaperman are you? Get the details—*get the whole story!*

TAYLOR: Yes, sir. (TAYLOR *hurriedly crosses to his desk and grabs his telephone.*)

HANK: Jimmy! Tell Smithy to make that a full-page sweep!

JIMMY: Yes, sir. (JIMMY *hurriedly crosses to the swinging doors and exits.* PHILLIPS *enters with papers and goes to his desk. Then the door to* WELCH'S *office opens and* WELCH *enters, looking across at* HANK.)

WELCH: Would you step in my office, Hank?

HANK: I'm busy right now . . . (*The phone rings and* HANK *answers. His face lights up.*) City Desk . . . Yes, Blondy . . . yeah, I'm listening . . . (*Pauses as he listens*) That's fine, Blondy . . . keep on it! (*Calls to* PHILLIPS) Take this call, Phillips—it's Blondy—he's got a story . . . (*As* HANK *hangs up,* WELCH *has crossed to within a few feet of his desk.*)

WELCH: It's important that I speak with you, Hank . . .

HANK: So is this story.

WELCH: It'll only take a minute. I'll be in my office. (*He returns to office.*)

HANK (*Rises reluctantly*): You men keep on that story! I want plenty of copy! (HANK *crosses to* WELCH'S *office and exits. As the door closes,* PHILLIPS, TAYLOR *and* RICHARDS, *sensing a scrap, exchange knowing glances. But the urgency of their work prevents them from talking.*)

PHILLIPS (*On phone*): Give me that again, Blondy! (*Starts making notes; his face is tense*) Five hundred on board! . . . ablaze from stem to stern! . . . (*Looks around at* RICHARDS *and* TAYLOR *awe-stricken*) Hold the presses! Simpson's boat is on fire.

CURTAIN

*   *   *

BEFORE THE CURTAIN: WELCH *enters from left, reading a newspaper.* HANK *enters from right and goes up to him.*

WELCH: I want to talk to you about your story on the Inland Excursions.

HANK: I thought that was what it was going to be.

WELCH: I'm afraid you're being a little too rough on the Alderman.

HANK: Rough? You haven't seen anything yet.

WELCH: Hank, I want you to drop that story.

HANK: But—it's true!

WELCH: Alderman Simpson admits that some improvements and repairs are necessary on the Inland Excursion boats, and he has assured me they will be done.

HANK: We can't do it! We can't drop the story!

WELCH: You seem to forget that a newspaper can't live without advertising. Inland Excursions is one of our best accounts.

HANK: You're forgetting your duty as a newspaper publisher! Those boats are rotten! The company is rotten!

WELCH: Stop it, Hank.

HANK: You know that when I write a story, I'm sure of the facts. If you don't back me up . . .

WELCH: I said stop it!

HANK: O.K., if that's the way you want it.

WELCH: I want you to listen to me. I want you to be reasonable . . .

HANK: Sorry—but I've heard all I want to hear. (HANK *moves toward right and* WELCH *moves after him.*)

WELCH: Hank! If you go out that door you're through! (HANK *stops, looks at* WELCH, *smiles and shrugs. Then he exits, right.* WELCH *exits left.*)

* * *

Scene 2

SETTING: *Same as Scene 1.*

AT RISE: TAYLOR, PHILLIPS *and* RICHARDS *are all talking at once on their telephones. The typewriters are going like mad.* JIMMY *is dashing from one desk to the other, gathering up copy. As* HANK *enters from* WELCH's *office, he pays no attention to the activity. He moves slowly to his desk and starts pulling the drawers out and piling things on top. The men do not notice the significance of* HANK's *movements, and* PHILLIPS *rushes to* HANK's *desk, a bunch of copy paper in his hand.*

PHILLIPS: Smithy wants to know about the column heads!

HANK: It doesn't matter.

PHILLIPS: *Doesn't matter?* (TAYLOR *and* RICHARDS *rush up to* HANK's *desk excitedly, each holding a batch of copy paper in his hands.*)

TAYLOR: Here's the latest! Five hundred women and children on board!

RICHARDS: . . . on fire from stem to stern!

TAYLOR: The water's full of people . . . lifeboats sank like lead! (*The full significance of the reporters' words sinks into* HANK's *mind. He reacts quickly and a tense, drawn look comes over his face as he grabs the copy paper from the reporters.*)

HANK: Who are the people?

PHILLIPS: Some Sunday School picnic. The boat is the *Seabird* of the Inland Excursions.

HANK: Now look, men—let's get all the facts together coolly and accurately. I want to know *what* Sunday School picnic was on the boat.

PHILLIPS: The Company doesn't know or won't tell us.

(*The telephone rings on* HANK's *desk and he tensely grabs the receiver.*)

HANK: City Desk! . . . Yes, Blondy . . . (*Pauses as he listens*) Taylor—take this! . . . The boiler just exploded!

TAYLOR: Yes, sir! (TAYLOR *rushes to his desk and grabs the telephone receiver.*)

HANK: Does anybody know the number of Inland Excursions?

PHILLIPS (*Hands* HANK *a paper*): Right here! I called them three times! The office is in a panic. (HANK *looks quickly at the telephone number and starts dialing.*)

HANK: Hello . . . This is the *City News*. What Sunday School was that you took out this morning? . . . (*Pause as he listens and his face tenses angrily*) Look it up while I hold the wire! *Don't* give *me* that line! I said— *look it up!* I want it *now*—N-O-W—while I'm talking to you! (*Pause*) Repeat that! Are you sure? . . . O.K. —thanks. (*As* HANK *hangs up the receiver, a sudden change comes over him. He takes a deep breath as if summoning his strength to recover from a blow.*)

PHILLIPS: Did they tell you?

HANK (*Nods*): The First Presbyterian Sunday School. Now get busy—call the Church and get the names. *All the names—understand!*

PHILLIPS: Yes, sir! (PHILLIPS *moves quickly to his desk and grabs the receiver on his telephone.* HANK *again takes a deep breath as if trying to throw off a great weight. As he picks up the telephone receiver and dials the composing room,* WELCH *exits from his office and moves to* HANK's *desk. As* HANK *talks to the composing room, he appears not to notice* WELCH *standing by his desk.*)

HANK (*Into phone*): Smithy? . . . Hank . . . How's the make-up coming? Twenty-one columns? . . . Yeah, sounds good. Now look, Smithy . . . we'll soon have a list of the dead—save two columns on the first page. I'll come down and show you what I mean! (*As* HANK *hangs up and rises from his chair,* WELCH, *a very much changed man, makes a penitent appeal.*)

WELCH: Hank . . . (*Then* TAYLOR *rushes excitedly up to the desk, handing* HANK *a sheaf of copy paper.*)

TAYLOR: Blondy's stuff! He's on the ball!

HANK (*Quickly glances at copy*): Good!

TAYLOR: The boat's been run aground! Blazing mass! Three hundred estimated dead—Blondy's shooting me a list of names . . .

HANK: Rush the names to me as they come in! Make sure the spelling is right!

TAYLOR: Yes, sir. (TAYLOR *quickly moves away to his desk and the telephone.* HANK *sinks down in his chair again, starts dialing a number, and doesn't pay any attention to* WELCH.)

WELCH: Hank—I'm sorry. I was wrong—

HANK (*Tersely*): Save it! Can't you see I'm busy! . . . (*He gets his connection and his voice changes.*) Hello— Agnes? This is Mr. Powell . . . What was the name of the Sunday School picnic Mrs. Powell and Ronald went on today? (*Pause*) Would you remember if I told you? Was it . . . was it the First Presbyterian? . . . You think so? But are you sure, Agnes? (*Pause*) Now listen carefully—if Mrs. Powell shouldn't get back this afternoon—call me. Be sure to call me. Goodbye. (HANK *hangs up the receiver, staring blankly before him.* WELCH *is still standing beside the desk, watching* HANK.)

WELCH: Hank—if there's anything I can do—anything! (HANK *gives* WELCH *a searching look, and without replying, rises from his chair and moves quickly to* TAYLOR'S *desk.* WELCH *walks slowly to his office and closes the door.*)

HANK: Did Blondy send in any names?

TAYLOR: I have thirty-two which have been identified . . . (HANK *picks up the copy paper and scans the list of names, then places it back on* TAYLOR'S *desk. The telephone rings and* TAYLOR *answers.*) Yes, Blondy—hold it a second. (*He cups his hand over the receiver as he speaks to* HANK) He's got more names . . .

HANK (*Tersely*): *Well*—take them down! I'm going to see Smithy—have them ready when I get back.

TAYLOR: Yes, sir. (HANK *turns, moves toward the swinging doors and exits.* TAYLOR *speaks again to* BLONDY *on the telephone*) O.K., Blondy—let's have the names . . . (*He writes on a copy paper as he listens*) What was that last one? . . . Yeah, I got Brewster . . . (*He continues writing down the names. Then a sudden tenseness comes to his face.*) Repeat that, Blondy—Are you sure? (*Pause*) Look, Blondy—call me back in five minutes. Hank's down in the press room. Besides I have to talk with the fellows—Yeah, five minutes! (TAYLOR *hangs up the receiver. His face is troubled as he speaks to* PHILLIPS *and* RICHARDS.) We're in a jam.

PHILLIPS: Leave *me* out of it.

TAYLOR: Blondy just gave me the name of Ronald Powell. (*In the background,* HANK *is seen to enter through the swinging doors.* TAYLOR, PHILLIPS *and* RICHARDS *do not see him approach.*)

PHILLIPS: Hank's kid?

RICHARDS: Are you sure?

TAYLOR: They haven't identified the body. But Blondy thinks . . .

HANK (*Calmly*): It's all right. I knew my wife—and my boy were on that boat. (*At the sound of* HANK's *voice,* TAYLOR, PHILLIPS *and* RICHARDS *turn, startled.*)

TAYLOR: Look, Hank—Blondy said there's no identification . . .

HANK: How did they know?

TAYLOR: They found a lunch box floating in the water. It had Ronald's name on it.

PHILLIPS: Take it easy, Hank.

HANK (*Gruffly*): Are you newspapermen, or shall we all sit down and have a good cry? We have to get out a paper! The forms close in fifteen minutes! (*He starts toward his desk, then turns back.*) Taylor—use these words on your list—Mrs. Hank Powell and her son, Ronald—twelve years old. (HANK *turns abruptly and crosses to his desk, where he busily writes and shuffles the piles of copy paper around. Without looking up, he calls to* TAYLOR, PHILLIPS *and* RICHARDS. *The men hurry to his desk.*) Give me your copy! Here's a chance to show whether you're journalists, or just reporters! (*The men hand their copy to* HANK *who gives the papers a fast reading.*) Here, Richards—arrange the display for all pages and number the columns *and* pages!

RICHARDS: Yes, sir!

HANK: All of you—make your stories snappy! Don't use "holocaust"—be original. And don't use "rats in a trap." Every sheet in town will use that! That's all! Get busy—only ten minutes before the forms close! (*For a moment the three men stand hesitant. It is obvious they are under a terrific strain. They want to say something, yet they cannot trust themselves to speak.*) I said—*get busy!* (*At the sound of* HANK'S *voice, the men hurry to their desks. As they leave,* HANK *slumps down in his chair. And then he clenches his fists in an effort to get a grip on himself. His quick, expert eyes scan the copy before him and he starts working—sheet after sheet of paper is deposited in a pile, ready for* JIMMY *to rush to the press room. At their respective desks,* TAYLOR, PHILLIPS *and* RICHARDS *are working, making a supreme effort to show their boss that they are newspapermen. The phone on* HANK'S *desk rings and* HANK *pays no attention to it. But the ringing continues and he listlessly lifts the receiver.*) City Desk . . . (*As he listens, excitement breaks over his face. He rises jubilantly, scattering papers to the floor*) Ann! . . . Ann! Where? . . . How? . . . Oh, Ann . . . (*Pause as he listens again*) You gave Ronald's lunch box to a neighbor to carry—and missed the boat? (*Another pause as he listens, and his attitude suddenly changes.*) Now you listen to me, Ann! This running around has got to stop! If it isn't church socials and bridge . . . it's something else! You and Ronald gallivanting off somewhere every day! . . . (*Pause, then angrily*) What's that? I don't care if it is vacation time! From now on you're staying home! Just you wait until I get there! (HANK *hangs up the receiver, a broad smile on his face. Then he looks at the pile of copy on his desk and yells out gruffly*) Copy! Will somebody tell me where that boy hides? (TAYLOR, PHILLIPS *and* RICHARDS *look across at* HANK *and grin.* WELCH *stands in the doorway to his office, also watching* HANK, *a smile of admiration on his face, as the curtains close.*)

THE END

Fires At Valley Forge

by Barrett H. Clark

Characters

THE SPEAKER
THE CORPORAL (O'MALLEY), *in his early thirties*
EPHRAIM COATES ⎫
JOSEPH JONES ⎪
WILLIAM EVANS ⎬ *youths, thirteen to sixteen years old*
BEN HOLDEN ⎭
AN AIDE, JAMES MONROE
GEORGE WASHINGTON
AN ORDERLY

SETTING: *An outpost in the woods near Valley Forge, early on a cold evening during the winter of 1778-79.*

AT RISE: *The action begins with the notes of a far-off bugle. A phonograph record may be used, or a real bugle, provided the sound comes as though from some distance away. This is followed by the entrance of the* SPEAKER, *who may either read his lines from a book or recite them.*

SPEAKER: Here is our place of action: a bare stage, as you see; no painted scenery, no colored lights, no fancy costumes. The story we are to act out before you needs no such trappings, and the author of it asks me to say that if you listen to the words our players speak, you can readily imagine what goes on, where our scene is laid, and why we offer it to you. You can see with your mind's eye the most vivid scene when it is described by a novelist in a book; and you can just as easily imagine on this platform the wintry background against which the players will act out this short episode. Everywhere about me is deep snow, which has drifted here and there, and behind me tall maples and firs and beeches. Over there— (*Points upstage, left*) just in front of a tall maple tree, a man crouches, trying to start a fire under a small pile of branches. (*Enter the* CORPORAL, *on the cue "tall maple," his coat collar turned up, blowing on his hands. He carries an old-fashioned musket, which he lays against a chair.*) The chair will suggest a small embankment of snow, a poor attempt to break the force of a biting north wind. That rag tied about his head is the only thing he can find to use for a hat, and the rags wrapped round his bleeding feet are what he calls his boots. Behind me, stretching as far as you can see, and much farther, are trees, spreading maples mostly, with scales of ice coating their trunks. The deep snow has drifted here and there, almost covering up the rail fences of a once flourishing farm, now abandoned. If you listen you can hear the wind.— We are in eastern Pennsylvania, among rolling hills, and the time of day is just after sunset. A few streaks of deep red and purple may still be seen over there. That is the West.— The man you see is a soldier. (*The* SPEAKER *retires just off stage, but facing the stage in view of the audience. The* CORPORAL, *having succeeded in starting his fire, picks up his musket wearily, as the* SPEAKER *recites his last lines. He paces painfully a few steps, then back again, occasionally blowing on his bare hands and stamping his feet. The* CORPORAL *turns to listen, then resumes his sentry-duty. After a moment he stops suddenly and looks off stage. Grips his musket, pauses, then speaks out gruffly, with an Irish accent.*)

CORPORAL: Who goes there? Who goes there, I say? (*Pause. A second later a* BOY *of thirteen or fourteen enters, carrying on his shoulder a staff with a rather large bundle tied to the end of it.*)

EPHRAIM: Don't shoot, man! I have no firearms!

CORPORAL: Stand where you are, then.

EPHRAIM (*Stopping*): I am, sir.

CORPORAL (*Aiming musket at him*): Not another step, I'm tellin' ye!

EPHRAIM: Where am I? Was that a bugle I heard?—Who are you?

CORPORAL: That's neither here nor there, lad. Give your name and business and be quick about it. Hey! Are there more of ye then? (*He raises his musket again as he sees three other* BOYS *peering at him behind* EPHRAIM.) Halt, every mother's son of ye! Are any of ye armed? Stand forth now, and be quick about it. (*The three other boys,* BEN HOLDEN, JOSEPH JONES, *and* WILLIAM EVANS, *advance uncertainly. Each of them also has a staff with a bundle attached to it. They all look tired.*)

BEN: Who is this fellow, lads? Some hunter, I'll be bound—

CORPORAL: Hunter, your granny! I'm Corporal O'Malley

of the Continental Army, a six months' volunteer whose
time has been up these four months past.

BEN (*Older than the others and surer of himself*): That's
what they all say. It's a fine excuse for deserters.

CORPORAL (*Advancing toward* BEN): Ye'll keep a civil
tongue in yer mouth, you. I tell ye I'd do right to be in
me home this instant settin' before me own kitchen
fire— Brr! (*Shivers.*)

JOSEPH: Surely he's a soldier, lads. Tell me, where are we,
sir?

CORPORAL: Ye're strangers in these parts, are ye? Well, this
magnificent blooming garden, this warm and pleasant
spot, is known hereabout as Valley Forge!

JOSEPH: Valley Forge! This—Valley Forge!

WILLIAM: But where is the Army?

EPHRAIM: Where is the camp?

BEN: This looks like no camp to me!

CORPORAL: Enough, lads! Stand back! Line up now, and
answer me questions. You— (*Pointing to* EPHRAIM.)
What's yer name, where do ye come from, and what's
yer business here?

BEN: Say nothing, Eph! Don't answer! Let us be on our
way.

EPHRAIM: I'm tired, Ben! (*To* CORPORAL) Ephraim Coates
is my name, and I live on a farm near Norristown, way
over yonder! We've been plowing through this snow for
the better part of two days and nights.

CORPORAL: It's maybe spies ye are—?

JOSEPH: I am Farmer Jones' youngest lad, and I live on the
Philadelphia Turnpike near the Coates farm.—My
name is Joseph Jones.

BEN: Why should we tell this fellow who we are? He may

be a spy himself. What affair is it of his? How do we know he tells the truth? This can't be Valley Forge! Where are the drilling soldiers, the tents, the uniforms?

CORPORAL (*Advances toward him, prodding him with the tip of his musket*): Young Master Impertinence, I'll learn ye manners if I have to beat them into ye! If you'll keep yer mouth closed and listen a minute, ye'll hear the men drillin' up there— (*Silence, then distant note of bugle.*) It's that new Dutchman, Baron Steuben. He don't know a word of any Christian language, but he's a great drillmaster: he'd drill the pants off every man in camp if they had any pants at all to their backs.— (BOYS *laugh.*) As for me own uniform, if you'll look careful— (*Points to his coat.*) you'll find a bit of a patch of faded blue on me somewhere. That's what's left of me fine military coat. If it's grand uniforms you'd be seein', off with ye this instant to Philadelphia town and gape at the red-coated dandies of General Howe's army. We're real soldiers here, and if our style don't suit ye, git out of here, or I'll warm yer backsides for ye!

BEN (*Laughing good-naturedly*): This fellow's a Patriot, and an American, wouldn't you know by the way he talks?—Corporal, accept my apologies.

CORPORAL: I will, then, for ye're a fine-spirited lad. So, who may ye be, and where d'ye come from now?

BEN: I'm Ben Holden; I was born in Bucks County, yonder, and I'm apprenticed to a printer in Philadelphia. Dr. Franklin himself gave me his blessing.

CORPORAL: Ye don't tell me! Dr. Franklin! My gal Nancy always reads me "Poor Richard's Almanac" every night at home on me farm. I'm not much of a reader myself. Makes *me* sleepy, ye know.

WILLIAM: And I'm William Evans. I live along the Delaware, near Trenton, and my father's a bootmaker.

CORPORAL (*Looks at his own "boots," then at* WILLIAM'S): A bootmaker, is it? Glory be, I've clean forgot what a boot looks like. Will you let me see now what you've got on? (WILLIAM *lifts up his boot and the* CORPORAL *admires it, measures it, then shakes his head.*) No, I thank ye kindly, it's too small for the likes of me, but I've a friend could use them boots—or maybe one of them, and one's better than none at all, I'm thinkin'.

EPHRAIM: Well, if you're satisfied we're not spies, may we warm ourselves by your fire? (*Other* BOYS *move across to fire as he speaks.*)

CORPORAL: Ye're welcome to it. There's plenty of wood hereabouts: it's not *that* we're worryin' about, it's the grub. So make yerselves comfortable. (*The four* BOYS *and* CORPORAL *gather round the fire.*) And what may ye have in them bags ye're carryin'?

WILLIAM: These be gifts for our friends here, and for my Pa. (WILLIAM *unties his bundle, and the other* BOYS *lay their staffs and bundles on the snow. In pantomime they clear away snow before the fire. The wind blows, and the* BOYS *show by gestures that they feel it.*) Woo-oh! The sun's gone down now!

CORPORAL: Sure it's the coldest February I've ever seen. (*To* JOSEPH) Is yer Pa here, lad? And who may he be?

JOSEPH: Lawrence Jones—he was *Private* Lawrence Jones last time we had word from him, and that was months ago. I've brought food here for him; my Ma cooked it —and a shawl, too— (*Brings forth a large knitted shawl and a few other things—simply paper packages, except the bread*)—she made this, and I've got a personal message. I want to see him, sir.

CORPORAL: Lawrence Jones, lad? What regiment did ye say—? No—wait— (*Pause*) Oh! (JOSEPH *is anxious.*) Lawrence—was he a short fellow? With a bit of a limp?—Ay—I remember—ye poor lad—I'm that sorry for ye— (*Pause*) Larry Jones was a brave man—

JOSEPH: *Was* a brave man, Corporal? What do you mean?

CORPORAL: Ye've heard, I'll warrant, that life in this camp is hard. Some of us live in huts here, if we're lucky enough to get huts; and we've no uniforms, and the food ain't hardly fit for beasts. The General told the honorable gentlemen of Congress there was three thousand of us here unfit for duty, because we're "barefoot, and *otherwise naked,*" but much good his tellin' 'em did. There's been sickness—and death, lad—for lots of us.

JOSEPH: But what about my Pa, sir?

CORPORAL: Yer Pa—well, yer Pa took sick and—he passed on like so many others—these two months ago. I'm sorry, lad; and sorry for yer Ma, Glory be!

JOSEPH (*Dazed*): I—I don't know what I can tell my Ma when I go home—I don't know! She's been expecting him now for a long while; his enlistment time was up before Christmas and we thought he'd be home then.

CORPORAL (*With a note of resentment*): *My* enlistment time's up too, I'm tellin' ye, and a lot of others here want to go back to their families and farms! But you can't fight a war without soldiers, and soldiers back home don't make an army. Sometimes *I'm* not so sure that anyone in these Colonies (besides myself and General Washington, mind ye!) wants this Liberty we're fightin' for! And I'm sometimes tempted—I might— (*Confidentially*) I say I *might*—pay a bit of a visit—

just to see my old woman and the younguns, and set the farm to rights—I *might,* but I ain't sayin'—

BEN (*Opening his sack, showing actual paper-wrapped objects, then looking at* CORPORAL): You say your name is O'Malley—?

CORPORAL (*Ignoring this and peering into the sack*): Bread! Fresh white bread! May I take just a squint at it?

BEN: I knew a Farmer O'Malley down our way, but he was *young.*

CORPORAL: I'm thirty-two, boy, but I'm thinkin' I look fifty now. (*Looking well at* BEN.) Hey! Don't I know *you*—ain't you that bold lad of Holden's that was always after stealin' me apples in the good days before the war!

BEN: Why—then you *are* Farmer O'Malley! Here— (*Offering bread, a real loaf*) this loaf was baked by your Missus, so it's yours by rights.

CORPORAL (*Eats a little from loaf*): Mine! Glory be! And how is my Missus, and Nancy, and Molly, and Mickey, and Katie and the baby? Tell me now, and don't keep me on pins and needles!

BEN: I saw them all and talked with them—'twas only three days ago. They're all in the best of health.

CORPORAL: Do they get on proper without me? Have they enough to eat, is it? Do they need me home, and do they miss me at all?

WILLIAM: Give the lad time to answer.

BEN: Your Missus begged us to say that you're to remain here with the General so long as he needs you, only she wants you back home at once!

CORPORAL: She's in trouble, do ye say?

EPHRAIM: No more than the rest of us, but she knows they need you in the army, so don't bother your head about anything else. There are men and women in our part— Tories and Loyalists—that want you to stop fighting; they say the Colonies can never win; that Howe and his army can lick you.

CORPORAL: Then why don't they try it? Lick us, is it? (*Grips his musket.*)

WILLIAM: The British army is waiting for spring to come; it's that they don't want to soil their grand uniforms, I reckon!

CORPORAL (*Having eaten more bread, turns to the* BOYS): And what other grand food have ye got maybe in them fine sacks of yours?

BEN: Come now, Corporal, we are here on more important business. It's getting cold and dark and we have a message for the General.

CORPORAL: Which one d'ye mean, now? There's more than *one* General here.

EPHRAIM: The head General, General Washington, of course.

CORPORAL: *His Excellency,* General Washington. Well, he don't see lads like you, so ye'd better leave yer things with me and I'll send them to His Excellency. (*He makes as though to gather up the sacks, but* JOSEPH, *who has stood silently by, goes up to him.*)

JOSEPH: Sorry, sir, but we were told special to deliver our message in person to General Washington.

CORPORAL: The General is engaged—weighty matters of state, they say—writing another letter to Congress, I'll be bound, though for the life of me I never could see no use of that. However, that's his business; he's an educated gentleman and my superior officer itself, and who am I to question his ways?

BEN: Lead us to him, Corporal, or we'll find the way ourselves. (*Each of the* BOYS *shoulders his staff and sack. The wind blows.*)

CORPORAL: Well, ye are an insistent crew of younguns, I must say. Stop here a minute now! Don't ye move, and I'll see what I can do fer ye, and if any stranger shows himself from that direction— (*Points right*) challenge him! (*He goes out carrying his musket. The* SPEAKER *walks toward center and addresses the audience. A bugle sounds again.*)

SPEAKER: They are still drilling, do you hear? For the good Baron Steuben knows that these troops are badly in need of discipline, and he is determined to restore their confidence. (*Bugle sounds.*) The bugle again! If you look up there (*Points up and left*) you will see tiny bright spots of orange and red through the trees: those are the fires kindled by the soldiers to sustain their courage when night comes. Over these cheery blazes they cook what poor food they can lay hands on. There is something cheerful about the dancing flames, and while few of the bedraggled wretches have time to think of anything but food and clothing and boots, when they gather about their bivouacs they feel just a little as though they were at home. Many of them at this hour of the evening picture to themselves their families gathered round huge open fireplaces, in broad low-ceilinged kitchens. The smoke from these campfires in the forest rises through tall trees; you can almost smell the burning logs—applewood, maple, fir.—Our friend the Corporal has sent word to one of the aides of General Washington, and he will be with us shortly. The Corporal, you will notice, realizes that he is in the presence of a commissioned officer and when he re-enters he stands stiffly at attention—over there. (*As a youthful* AIDE *enters and looks at the* BOYS, *the* SPEAKER *goes back to his former position downstage right.*)

AIDE: Well, Corporal, are these the lads? (BOYS *stand at attention, and inspect the* AIDE.)

EPHRAIM: Yes, your honor.

AIDE: Major, lads, Major Monroe, Aide to General Washington.

WILLIAM: We came here, sir—well, sir—we thought you might want to know—that is, sir, to bring words of cheer to some of the men, and the father of this lad, Joseph Jones.—And here (*He and the other* BOYS *show their sacks*) we have some food and a few clothes—

AIDE (*Interested*): Food, lads? Did you say food?

BEN: Ay, sir, fresh-baked bread. (AIDE *nods his satisfaction.*) And cinnamon buns, some bacon, and an English plum pudding—

AIDE (*Mock serious*): *English?*

BEN: Your pardon, sir, *American* plum pudding.

AIDE: Let that pass, for I doubt if I could resist the temptation to eat even the most English of English plum puddings.

WILLIAM (*Just touching sacks, but showing nothing*): And here, sir, are stockings—

EPHRAIM: And boots.

BEN: And a jacket. (*The* AIDE *is interested, and a little amused. Starting to take one of the sacks.*)

AIDE: The Corporal will take these bags to Headquarters and the Quartermaster will see to the distribution of the food and clothing—

WILLIAM: Your pardon, sir, but my Ma said I was to convey these direct to the General—er—to His Excellency —to General Washington in person—together with our message.

AIDE: But I am the General's Aide, lads, and His Excellency is unusually busy—

BEN: Ay, we know: his letter to the Congress, but my Pa says—begging your pardon—that Congress is a pack of fatheads that pay no attention to those fine letters the General writes—

AIDE (*Smiles*): That is a matter which only His Excellency may judge. Now, if you will permit me I shall take these things to—well, I promise to convey them direct to His Excellency, and if you will speak the message to me I will undertake to deliver it verbatim—

WILLIAM: How is that, sir—ver—?

AIDE (*Smiles*): "Word for word." A Latin expression.

BEN: Well, I have the message, but I don't feel I can give it to anyone else. So if you don't mind, I'd rather tell as much of it as I can recall to His Excellency.

AIDE: This is most irregular. The Commander-in-Chief has a thousand things to attend to.—However (*Smiles and starts left*), I will see what can be done—(*Boys eagerly exclaim*) but mind you, I promise nothing. (*He turns and goes out.*)

WILLIAM: Think ye he'll come here?

BEN: No doubt he will.

JOSEPH: What should we do? Stand stiff like this?

EPHRAIM: My knees are trembling. They say the General is seven foot tall.

WILLIAM: Surely *he* will have a fine uniform?

EPHRAIM: I saw a likeness of him one time, with a great

sword, and gold braid, and he was riding on a grand white horse.

BEN: He'll have no white horse here, and I'll warrant even *his* uniform will need mending. (*The* BOYS *spruce up somewhat, and use their staffs to present arms, as though they were muskets. The* CORPORAL *pokes the fire. He, too, is impressed by the solemnity of the occasion, and adjusts his "hat."*)

CORPORAL: He *may* come, me lads, and then again he mayn't, but if he does, I warn you one thing: If ye dare open yer mouths or let out a peep about me and me personal troubles, and me short rations, and me time bein' up, and wantin' to go home—which I *don't!*—I'll break yer blessed necks fer ye. Attention! Here comes someone. (*They all stand at attention. Bugle call in the distance.*)

SPEAKER (*Standing out again*): The Headquarters of the Commander-in-Chief of the Continental Army stands not far off through the wood, covered with snow. Just before that bugle call you heard, the General left Headquarters accompanied by his Aide, and made his way through the woods. Look for an instant at the high trees, swaying in the night wind, and the twinkle of distant campfires. There are more of them now: the night is alive with them. I hear a dead branch fall. (*Pause*) Someone is coming! (*The* SPEAKER *retires. Enter the* AIDE *left, carrying an old-fashioned lantern. Stands at attention, and announces.*)

AIDE: His Excellency General Washington. (WASHINGTON, *played by a mature boy of quiet dignity, enters and advances a little toward center, past the* AIDE. *The* BOYS, *at rigid attention, fall back two or three steps; the* CORPORAL, *upstage, is also at attention.* WASHINGTON *has no*

*sword, nor hat, nor is he dressed in any way different
from that of a modern man in a plain "business suit."
He is dignified, without being the least bit stiff. There
is a touch of quiet dry humor in his manner at first.*)

WASHINGTON: Are these the lads, Major?

AIDE: These are the lads, Your Excellency (*Pointing to
them in turn*): Benjamin Holden, Ephraim Coates, William Evans, and Joseph Jones. Jones is the son of Private
Jones, sharpshooter of the 27th Pennsylvania—Larry
Jones, whom Your Excellency will remember—the one
who—

WASHINGTON (*Advancing to* JOSEPH): Larry Jones? Ay—
young man, you will convey to your mother my heart-
felt condolences, and inform her that her husband—
your father—died the death of a devoted patriot.

JOSEPH (*At attention*): Y-yes, sir. (*Hides his head in his
arm.* WASHINGTON *gently takes the* BOY'S *staff and sack,
and lays them on the snow. He then turns to the others.*)

WASHINGTON: You may all take your ease— (*The* BOYS
awkwardly set down their staffs and sacks.) And now, to
what do I owe the honor of this somewhat unusual visit
to our Headquarters? (BOYS *are rather embarrassed.*)
Come, who is your spokesman? (*The* OTHERS *urge* BEN
forward.)

BEN: I, sir. I'm Ben Holden from near Trenton, apprenticed to a printer in Philadelphia, and blessed by Dr.
Franklin in person. These lads and I are loyal Americans, sir. We have come here with what food and clothing we could carry—but—but I'm afraid it's not much
—seeing your great need: a jacket, some fresh bread
(*The* CORPORAL *gives a slight start*), a pair of boots
made by Willy's father, a shawl—

JOSEPH: My Mother knitted that for my Pa.

BEN (*To* JOSEPH): Don't interrupt me, Jo—I cannot remember my speech—

WASHINGTON: We are grateful to you, lads. This is bitter weather, and you must have come all of forty miles.

WILLIAM: 'Twas nearer fifty, Your Excellency; we went from farm to farm, sir; the Patriots begged us to bring other things, but this was all we could carry, and hard carrying it was.

WASHINGTON: And now will you do me the kindness of telling me why you wished to see me in person?

EPHRAIM: Our Pas and Mas instructed us to make sure you got these things, and—and they wanted you to know they were that grateful to you and your men for fighting for them.

BEN: You weren't to think, because you didn't hear about us, we were losing heart or had forgotten you. And we wanted to tell you that the British in Philadelphia have no wish to fight—

WASHINGTON: You amaze me. Proceed—tell me more—

BEN: We don't *know* that for a fact, sir; but we've listened to their soldiers talk, and they prefer to dance, and drink, and not risk their skins in battle. They may be brave, sir, but their heart's not in it. *So* they say. But we Americans feel different, sir, and so do the farming and working folks—the folks on *our* side.

WASHINGTON: Believe me, lads, this is most gratifying.— You are doubtless disappointed to see us here in rags (*the front* of my uniform is fairly presentable, but I must take care not to turn around!); we are without tents, without proper food; no parades, no music, no gold braid; true, our enemies have such things, in abundance, but are they winning this war? Not yet! True, we need supplies, and we must have them—but forgive this

interruption: I offer my apologies to the young man—
(*Indicating* BEN.) You had a message for me?

BEN: I'm afraid, sir, it's gone clean out of my head. Besides, 'twas not so fine as it sounded when I was learning
the words by myself—er—verbatim.

WASHINGTON: I beg you, convey the idea in your own fash-
ion. Have no fear.

BEN: Well, sir, our friends and families, knowing you were
in difficulty, would have you know that even the young
and the old, and the women, and the lads and girls are
—I can't recall the words—are with you. We live amongst
many still loyal to the King, and my Pa declares you
ought to know this, and take courage. We tried in the
autumn to send you horses and food but they were captured and sold, sometimes by British raiders, but oftener
by those that were born here and should, by rights, be
helping us. We know your men are deserting, that they
want news of their wives, and families, and farms; but
we lads are trying to do our part, and my Ma declares
I'm the head of our family now; and—and—these things
— (*Points to sacks on the ground*) they seem so little,
and you need so much—and—I'm right sorry, sir, I
can't say more—

WASHINGTON: What you *have* said means more to me than
a hundred wagons of food or clothing. This is evidence
of that spirit of Liberty without which we cannot hope
to win our freedom. I have sometimes despaired of our
cause, and I wonder— (*His voice trails off. The* BOYS
*don't interrupt him. The bugle again in the distance.
This rouses* WASHINGTON. *To* CORPORAL, *who has begun
to doze*.) Corporal! (CORPORAL *jumps to attention*.)
You will take these things to Headquarters and see that
they are divided amongst the sick according to the needs

of each. I take it that you, Corporal, are partial to good white bread?

CORPORAL: Excellency—! (WASHINGTON *extracts part of loaf which the* CORPORAL *had stuffed into his clothes.*)

BEN: Your pardon, Excellency, I gave him that bread; it was his own Missus that baked it.

WASHINGTON (*To* AIDE): Major, under the circumstances we may, I think, dispense with the usual court-martial?

CORPORAL (*Saluting*): Thank ye, Your Excellency. (*Begins to pick up the sacks, at which* JOSEPH *runs to him and takes out the shawl.*)

JOSEPH (*Hesitating, as he stands at attention before* WASH-INGTON): Your—Your Excellency, this shawl is the one my Ma knitted for my Pa, and now—now that he won't need it—

WASHINGTON: Proceed.

JOSEPH: I wondered, it would please my Ma—are you ever cold, Your Excellency?

WASHINGTON: I am often cold, lad.

JOSEPH: Then would you—would you oblige me by taking this for yourself?

WASHINGTON (*Touched*): I am indeed obliged to *you,* and to your esteemed Ma as well. (*Takes shawl and looks at it carefully.*) 'Tis excellently knitted.—If you agree not to inform Mistress Washington, I will say that Her Excellency could not have made a better one herself. (*Wraps shawl about his neck. The* CORPORAL *stares at him open-mouthed.* CORPORAL *then picks up the sacks and, after an attempt at a salute, marches off left.* WASHINGTON *turns to the* BOYS.) I would offer you the hospitality of our camp, my young friends, but this spot is just as warm and, I fear, somewhat cleaner than what you would find up yonder in the woods, so make yourselves comfortable round the fire. The Corporal will return directly, I hope, but he looks somewhat sleepy. You will oblige me by helping him stand guard tonight.

BOYS (*Excited*): Ay, sir!—We'll be honored.—Indeed, we will, sir!

BEN: Please, sir, I've just remembered my speech; I think I have it proper now.

WASHINGTON (*A hand on his shoulder*): You have already told me everything—and indeed 'twas a most proper speech—and will you convey to your friends and families my gratitude, and that of the Army?—Now, Major, back to our drills; Baron Steuben will upbraid us for being absent so long—without his leave!

AIDE: I shall esteem it a pleasure to hear him translate his profanity into bad French, and wait until the interpreter turns it into improper English! (WASHINGTON *turns to go out with* AIDE. WILLIAM *steps forward.*)

WILLIAM: Sir?

WASHINGTON (*To* AIDE): One moment, Major. Yes, lad?

WILLIAM: Sir, my Pa will tell you I am the best shot in our part of the county, and I—I would like, sir, to be a soldier with you.

WASHINGTON: You are only a boy.

WILLIAM: I'm—I'm sixteen, sir.

WASHINGTON: Can that be possible? (*Looks at him severely.*)

WILLIAM: Well, sir, I shall be *fifteen* next June. (*An* ORDERLY *comes in and stands at attention.*)

WASHINGTON (*Impatiently*): Speak your message, man.

ORDERLY: General Von Steuben's compliments, sir. The General requests Your Excellency's presence at the new drill; the men, he declares, are becoming most impatient.

WASHINGTON: My compliments to the General. Pray inform him that I shall be delayed another three minutes. (*The* ORDERLY *salutes and goes out.*)

BEN: Sir, do you require a drummer boy? I—

JOSEPH: I can shoot straighter than Will, sir, and I really *am* sixteen—

EPHRAIM: Would you permit me to shine Your Excellency's boots—? (*The above three speeches are almost simultaneous.* WASHINGTON *raises one arm in a gesture of admonishment, and the* BOYS *are silent.*)

WASHINGTON: Lads—or, rather, young men—it is natural that you should wish to help us fight our good fight, and I shall not try to make you think I am displeased. This war can be won only if a sufficient number of us are determined to win it; if we think and feel freedom, if we give our soldiers the courage to see through to the end what they have undertaken. It is not my part to decide whether war in itself is right or wrong, though I am of the opinion of my old friend Dr. Franklin, who declared that there never was a good war nor a bad peace. I have been put in command of a ragged rabble of farmers, blacksmiths, ministers of the Gospel, schoolmasters, and a few gentlemen, like the young Marquis de La Fayette, who is at this moment catching his death of cold instructing a company of soldiers how to keep step—with the snow three feet deep as you see, and a bitter wind blowing. There is something about us— about you and me, about your Pas and Mas—that cannot and, by Heaven, *will* not, suffer the command of any master. We Americans find it hard to take orders. It is this square-headed stubbornness that has enabled us to fight the enemy when we had to, and retreat before him when we thought that best; and it is the same spirit

that, God willing, shall bring us victory. I can find soldiers to fight our battles if you at home keep on *wanting* us to win. Look at our campfires; they are lighted
every night.—When you sit before your own fires, remember us here, or wherever we may be hereafter.
Think, lads, that the flames you kindle are of the same
essence that we kindle, that your flame at home is our
flame at Valley Forge, or wherever we shall be en-
camped. You at home are even more necessary than we.
And for these reasons, Will, and Ben, and Ephraim,
and Joseph, I thank you from the bottom of my heart,
and I accept your offer (*The* BOYS *are delighted*), but I
shall not take you into the Army; proceed as you have
begun, and when this war is over there will be, I promise you, much more for you to do than could be done at
this time. War destroys! It is for you and your brothers
and sisters, and your children after you, to make full
and proper use of this thing we call Liberty. Possibly—
possibly, I say, your descendants may find some means
to settle their differences without killing those who disagree with them.—And now, my time is up. Young men
—fellow soldiers—you will be gone in the early morning; convey my respectful compliments to your people,
and my thanks, and remember that you are all soldiers
with us in this struggle. (*The* BOYS *stand at attention,
deeply moved, but utter no sound. They go right, find
places in the snow, under the trees, lie down, and are
soon asleep. The* CORPORAL *returns, having delivered
the sacks. He picks up and distributes the staffs among
the sleeping boys; covers them up in pantomime, and
comes back to* WASHINGTON, *who has been standing in a
thoughtful attitude.* WASHINGTON *draws his shawl tight
around his neck: the wind has risen again. The* COR-

PORAL *comes close to* WASHINGTON *and almost kneels at his feet, laying his musket on the ground.* WASHINGTON *is not surprised. He lifts him up until the* CORPORAL *stands facing him, as* WASHINGTON *speaks quietly.*) O'Malley!

CORPORAL: Sir?

WASHINGTON: Patrick O'Malley.

CORPORAL: Sir! You know my first name, then?

WASHINGTON: You're homesick, man.

CORPORAL: I *was,* sir, God forgive me!

WASHINGTON: You are wondering about your wife and family.

CORPORAL: I *was,* Excellency, but the boys brought me grand news.

WASHINGTON: And fresh bread, too?

CORPORAL: I shouldn't have et it, sir—but Glory be—!

WASHINGTON: Your wife baked it for you?

CORPORAL: I didn't mean to, sir.

WASHINGTON (*After a short pause*): Patrick, when were you intending to leave us?

CORPORAL (*Supplicating*): Forgive me, sir, I was that worried!

WASHINGTON (*Severely*): You are aware what we call that crime in the army?

CORPORAL: Yes—yes—sir.

WASHINGTON: And the penalty for it?

CORPORAL: Y-yes, sir. Please, please don't disgrace me! I couldn't stand that. I'll never think of going away again! I got to worryin' about the farm, and Nancy and Mickey and all—

WASHINGTON: I have not seen *my* farm for years, either.

CORPORAL: Is *your* time up, Excellency?

WASHINGTON (*With the shadow of a smile*): It cannot be

up until this struggle is over, and victory achieved. You are a trusted sentry, Patrick; upon you may depend the safety of our camp. If you ever consider leaving us again, will you come to me, in person, and inform me?

CORPORAL (*Taking* WASHINGTON'S *hand for a second and letting it drop*): Oh, I will, Excellency!—For the love of all the saints, sir, I'd not want a livin' soul to know about me goin' to desert.

WASHINGTON (*Resuming his dignity and severity*): Corporal!

CORPORAL (*At attention*): Your Excellency?

WASHINGTON: I did not hear one word of what you have just told me.

CORPORAL (*Gratefully*): Excellency, I will never forget one word of what *you* have just told *me!* (*Stoops to pick up his musket, and shivers as* WASHINGTON *is about to go.* WASHINGTON *notices, and as* CORPORAL *is still stooping, unwinds the shawl from his own neck, and puts it round the* CORPORAL'S *shoulders. The* CORPORAL *silently and proudly allows* WASHINGTON *to do this.* WASHINGTON *then goes out left, and the* CORPORAL, *his musket on his shoulder, begins pacing back and forth. The bugle sounds in the distance. As the* CORPORAL *marches upstage, he is no longer the center of interest, and quietly slips out. Then the* SPEAKER *walks to the center of the stage and addresses the audience.*)

SPEAKER: And that is all. You cannot read this little story in your history books, for it is not there, yet such a thing *might* have happened; for all of us, people like you and me, are the stuff of which history is made, though very little of it is remembered or set down in black and white. We know that over a hundred and fifty years ago Washington and his officers and his men did thus and so, but what the boys and girls, the wives and daughters did, was neither very exciting nor very spectacular; yet, as we have tried to show you, that is the kind of thing that helped win that freedom which we of today accept as naturally as the air we breathe, that precious and inalienable right to call our bodies and our souls our own, and to resist at whatever cost any man, party, or nation that seeks to deprive us of it. (*He stands still for a moment, then turns and walks off.*)

THE END

Catastrophe Clarence

by Maxine Shore

Characters

BOB MEADOWS, *about 13*
ANDY THOMPSON, *his pal*
PROFESSOR WADSWORTH W. CLARK, *Bob's astronomer uncle*
HOWARD, *the professor's chef and housekeeper*
GLENN MATTHEWS, *the professor's secretary and assistant*
CATASTROPHE CLARENCE, *Space Man of the Universal Meteor Patrol*

TIME: *A summer evening.*
SETTING: *Professor Clark's observatory in the San Bernardino Mountains.*
AT RISE: BOB *and* ANDY *enter from door left, carrying luggage.* BOB *is also carrying a dusty quart jar very carefully.*

ANDY (*Setting down his suitcase*): Gee, what a neat place! I've never been in an observatory before.
BOB: My uncle built it himself, to carry on special research.
ANDY: But where is he?
BOB: Oh, he's around somewhere—probably in his office

in the next room. I guess no one heard us come in. (*Sets down suitcase and flops into comfortable chair*) We'll look him up in a minute. Right now, I just want to take a breather.

ANDY (*Sitting on suitcase*): Yeah. That was a long hike through the woods, and uphill all the way. Your uncle ought to have a road built up here.

BOB: He doesn't want one. Says he gets more privacy this way.

ANDY: I'll bet. (*Enter* HOWARD, *the professor's chef and housekeeper, from door right. He wears horn-rimmed glasses, chef's hat and a confused look.*)

HOWARD: Oh, professor! I thought I heard— (*Stops and stares at boys*) Well, who are you? How'd you get in here?

BOB: You remember me, Howard. I'm Bob Meadows, the professor's nephew, and this is my friend, Andy Thompson. (ANDY *rises politely*) Andy, this is Howard. He does the cooking here.

ANDY: How do you do?

HOWARD: Hello, young man. But—the professor didn't tell me you were coming—

BOB: *You* were supposed to tell *him* we were coming, Howard. I telephoned a couple of days ago from Los Angeles, long distance. You answered the phone, don't you remember? You said the professor and Mr. Matthews were both busy in the observatory, and you'd take the message and would let us know if it wasn't okay for us to come. Don't you remember?

HOWARD (*Pushing back chef's hat and scratching head*): Well, I do remember some sort of conversation about a visit—but—

BOB: But you forgot to tell Uncle Wadsworth, didn't you?

Gosh, Howard, it's professors who're supposed to be absent-minded, not cooks! (*Enter* PROFESSOR WADSWORTH W. CLARK, *from door right.*)

PROFESSOR: Why, Bob! What a pleasant surprise! Where on earth did you come from? And who's this young man with you?

HOWARD (*Helpfully*): He's Bob's brother, isn't that nice?

BOB: No, no, Howard. He's my friend, Andy Thompson.

HOWARD (*Not hearing right*): They don't look much alike, do they, professor? You'd never guess they were twins.

ANDY: No, no. You don't understand. I'm not Bob's—

PROFESSOR (*Smiling*): Never mind. I understand. Howard gets a bit absent-minded sometimes.

HOWARD (*Indignantly*): I do not. (*Looks about vaguely*) Now, let's see, what did I come in here for? Oh, I guess I meant to go into the kitchen and—and scrub out the bathtub. (*Exits*)

PROFESSOR: Howard's a bit confused sometimes, I'm afraid, but he means well. (*Turns to boys*) Now, Bob, tell me how you boys happen to be here. Who brought you?

BOB: My dad. He had to go to Barstow on a business trip and this was only a little out of his way. You asked me to come up any time I could this summer and bring one of my friends—

PROFESSOR (*Heartily*): Of course, Bob, and I'm very glad to see you and your friend Andy. Too bad your father couldn't stop, too.

BOB: He was in a hurry to keep an appointment and didn't have time. He dropped us off down below. We called long distance a couple of days ago, Uncle Wadsworth, and talked to Howard. I guess he forgot to tell you.

PROFESSOR: Well, it doesn't really matter. I like surprises.
Now that you're here, I hope you'll enjoy yourselves,
boys.

BOB: Oh, we will! But—we've come to see you on business, sort of, too.

PROFESSOR: Business?

ANDY: Yes, sir. You see, we've got a problem.

PROFESSOR: A problem? What is it, boys?

BOB (*Holding up jar*): It's in this jar here.

PROFESSOR (*Puzzled*): But—it looks empty!

ANDY: It isn't, though. It's full of smog—from Los Angeles.

BOB (*Holds up jar and unscrews top*): Sure—see?

PROFESSOR: Uh—yes, I see. I mean, I smell. (*Coughs*)

ANDY: Close it up quick, Bob, before it all leaks out.

PROFESSOR: Yes, please do, Bob, before it pollutes our nice
pure mountain air. But I'm afraid I still don't see just
what—

BOB (*Screwing top back on*): We want you to analyze it for
us. Andy's dad says if the smog gets any worse, he'll
move to Alaska—

ANDY: And I don't want to move. I like it here in California.

BOB: I don't want Andy to move, either. He's my best
friend.

PROFESSOR: But, boys, you don't understand. I'm not—I
can't—

BOB: I told Andy what a famous scientist you are, Uncle
Wadsworth, and about all the awards you've won. I told
him you could find out what makes smog and we could
tell the mayor of L.A. and then he could get rid of it.

PROFESSOR: But, boys, I'm an astronomer, not a smog
analyst—

BOB: But—I thought you knew everything—

PROFESSOR: I'm afraid not. I'd like to help you, Bob, but this is out of my line. But—how about something to eat? You boys must be hungry after your long trip.

ANDY: We sure are!

BOB: I'm starved! (*Sets quart of smog disgustedly on table. Enter* HOWARD.)

HOWARD: Professor, how do you want your eggs this morning—scrambled or poached? And would your nephews like oatmeal or corn flakes?

ANDY: Corn flakes—for *dinner?*

PROFESSOR (*Patiently*): Howard—look out the window.

HOWARD (*Doing so*): Why, it's dark out! Must be another thunderstorm coming up. And it started out to be a real nice day, too.

PROFESSOR: No, Howard. It's dark out because it's night. Dinnertime.

HOWARD: Well, now, is that right? How time flies. I'd better go right out and start the potatoes. (*Exits*)

PROFESSOR (*Sighs*): Well, it looks as if dinner will be a little late again tonight. While we're waiting, perhaps you boys would like to look through the telescope.

ANDY: Gee! That would be keen. I'd love to look through it, sir.

BOB: Go ahead, then, Andy. I've seen it lots of times.

PROFESSOR (*Beckons*): Come on, Andy, have a look at our marvelous solar system.

ANDY: Gee, thanks! (*Goes to telescope.* PROFESSOR *adjusts it.*) Wow! Millions of stars!

PROFESSOR (*Smiling*): Correction. Trillions. And they're not all stars, either, my boy. Some of them are planets, some are comets, some spiral nebulae, and still others may be meteors.

ANDY: What's the difference—they all shine.

PROFESSOR (*Clearing throat*): There's a vast difference. A star, for instance, is any self-luminous celestial body exclusive of comets, meteors and nebulae.

ANDY (*Politely, as he continues to look through telescope, fascinated*): Oh, I see.

PROFESSOR: Planets are much smaller than stars, and shine by reflected light.

ANDY: Planets are smaller than stars? I always thought it was the other way around.

PROFESSOR: Oh, no, Andy. The sun, for example, is a star of about average brightness and size, while the Earth, Mars, Venus, Jupiter, Neptune, Saturn and so on are planets.

ANDY: How about the moon?

BOB (*Settled comfortably in armchair*): Oh, I know that. The moon is a satellite.

ANDY: Well, it may only be a satellite, but it sure looks big through this telescope! A little closer and I bet I could see the people walking around on it.

PROFESSOR: It's extremely doubtful that life could exist on the moon or any other planet except, perhaps, in its very lowest forms.

ANDY: How do you know? Nobody's ever been there, have they?

PROFESSOR (*Clearing throat*): No, Andy, but astronomers have made certain scientific deductions from known atmospheric facts.

ANDY: How's that again?

BOB: Well, I don't know, Uncle Wadsworth. I bet there could be people just like us living up there somewhere. Why not?

ANDY: Sure, why not? Why should we think we're the only

planet in the whole universe that's inhabited? That's
—conceited! (*Enter* GLENN MATTHEWS, *the professor's
assistant, with notebook.*)

GLENN: Why, hello there, Bob! Glad to see you. I just met
Howard and he said something about visitors. The professor's twin nephews, I believe he said, but—

BOB: Hi, Glenn. Howard got it all mixed up, as usual. He
thinks my friend, Andy Thompson here, is my twin
brother. Can't talk him out of it. You know Howard!

GLENN (*Grinning*): You bet I know Howard. But I doubt
if he knows me yet, even though I've been the professor's assistant for over a year. He's still confused about
me.

PROFESSOR (*Smiling*): Never mind. Howard's an excellent
cook.

GLENN (*Nodding*): True. Even if we do get cereal for
dinner oftener than steak.

ANDY (*Groaning*): I was afraid of that. I don't even like
cereal for *breakfast*.

GLENN: Well, you'll like things here. For breakfast, we
often have fried chicken. With ice cream for dessert.

ANDY: Wow! That's for me!

GLENN: Professor, about these notes you dictated yesterday
regarding the rings of Saturn—I have a few questions
and—

PROFESSOR: All right, Glenn. I'll go over them with you in
the office right now, before dinner. Will you excuse us,
boys? You can entertain yourselves here all right until
we eat, can't you?

ANDY: Sure! I love looking through this telescope!

PROFESSOR: Oh. We'd better take these suitcases to your
room, boys—you know which one, Bob. (*Picks up luggage*)

BOB: Sure. Thanks, Uncle Wadsworth.

GLENN: Here, let me take them, sir. (*Takes them from* PROFESSOR *as the two go out*)

ANDY (*Whistling*): Well, what do you know! Huh! Say, Bob, look here!

BOB: Huh—where? What do you see? People on the moon? (*He crosses to telescope and stands beside* ANDY.)

ANDY: Sorry, no people. But there's a real bright red star here that I'm sure I didn't see a minute ago. Gosh, it's pretty! Looks just like the taillight on my bike!

BOB: Let's see. (*Looks*) Say, that's neat! It looks like it's moving, too, coming right this way. Maybe—maybe it's a—a flying saucer!

ANDY: Gosh—do you suppose it could be? I've always wanted to see a flying saucer. Let me look at it again, Bob. Wait until we tell the professor! (ANDY *keeps on peering through the telescope while* BOB *waits impatiently for another turn. The* SPACE MAN's *head appears in the window at the rear, but at first the two boys are too absorbed with the telescope to see him. The* SPACE MAN *looks all around, then hops into the room.*)

CLARENCE: Wow! What an experience! Where am I? (ANDY *continues to stare through the telescope excitedly and doesn't notice, but* BOB *turns and sees the visitor.*)

BOB: Hey! Who are you? What kind of an outfit is that you're wearing, anyway? Who're you masquerading as, Superman?

CLARENCE: I asked a question of you first. Where, exactly, am I?

BOB: Why, you're in Professor Wadsworth W. Clark's observatory, that's where. And I don't think my uncle will like your hopping in through the window that way.

And what a crazy-looking costume! (*Circles him curiously*)

CLARENCE: But—what planet is this?

BOB: What planet? Why, Earth, of course! Are you kidding? What're you all rigged out like that for? Oh, I know! I bet Uncle Wadsworth is playing a joke on us. Ha, ha! Wait'll Andy gets a load of you. He'll die laughing! Hey, Andy! Look at him! (ANDY *turns reluctantly from telescope.*)

ANDY: Gosh! A real space man!

CLARENCE (*Nodding*): Right, earth boy! You're a smart one. I am a real space man. They call me Catastrophe Clarence from Clarion. I'm attached to the Universal Meteor Patrol, a very select outfit, I'll have you know. (*Struts a little*)

BOB (*Incredulously*): You mean, you're for real?

ANDY: Sure he is, Bob. Can't you tell? But what I want to know is (*Advances suspiciously*) what's he doing here on earth? Is this an invasion from outer space? Come on, Bob—let's rush him!

CLARENCE: Wait, earth boys, wait! Not so fast. Hold it! You don't understand. Stop! Stop, I say! (*They have started forward to tackle him, but now they fall as if blocked by an invisible wall.*)

BOB (*Sits up and rubs his head*): Ouch—my head! What hit me? Wh—what happened?

CLARENCE (*Apologetically*): Sorry, earth boys, you ran into my energy wall. I had to put it up to protect myself. You wouldn't wait for my explanation. I'm not leading any invasion of your earth. You earth people are always too suspicious of strangers. The rest of the universe wants to be friendly, but you're too excitable.

ANDY (*Ruefully rubbing his leg*): I guess you're right.

BOB (*Getting to his feet again and pulling* ANDY *up, too*): But you still haven't told us why you're here.

CLARENCE (*Slowly*): Well, it's kind of an embarrassing story. As I said, I'm on duty with the Universal Meteor Patrol. I was cruising along out in space on regular patrol duty when I got too interested in looking at a Man from Earth in a comic book I'd brought along from home—the planet Clarion—and I kind of lost track of what I was doing. First thing I knew, this meteor was streaking toward earth. It's the business of the Universal Meteor Patrolmen to keep dangerous meteors away from inhabited planets, you know. Then I realized I was running out of litronium, too, and had forgotten to bring along my extra supply from the base.

ANDY: Gee! How terrible!

BOB: Then what happened?

CLARENCE: What happened? I was so close to earth by this time that I got caught in the gravitational pull and couldn't get free because my litronium was so low and I was too weak.

ANDY: That must have been tough! You say you fell toward earth? You don't seem hurt.

CLARENCE: Oh, I'm not. Fortunately, I had just enough litronium left to float down easily. (*Sighs*) But what worries me now is that the meteor is out of control and all the Space officials will blame me for letting it crash into the earth. I may be grounded on Clarion for life!

BOB: You mean that meteor is going to—crash?

ANDY: What'll it do to earth?

CLARENCE (*Sadly*): It may destroy your entire planet, I'm afraid. Or at least this hemisphere. And all of us have had so much fun studying your Earth, too. No planet in the universe is as full of crazy characters as this one is! It's a museum piece.

ANDY: But that's terrible!

BOB: Yes! Can't you do something—before it's too late?

CLARENCE (*Shakes head*): Not unless I can find some litronium some place quickly.

BOB: What's litronium?

ANDY: We never heard of it before.

CLARENCE: What's litronium! Why, that's the stuff that gives us Space Patrolmen the energy and courage we need to meet every obstacle—to fly, jump a mile, keep alert!

BOB: You mean it's some kind of fuel—or food?

CLARENCE: Without litronium, no one could steer the comets and meteors safely away from the planets. Litronium's nourishment.

ANDY (*Puzzled*): You mean—like hot dogs?

CLARENCE: Hot dogs?

BOB: Wieners, frankfurters. We eat 'em. (*Opens mouth, gestures*) We put 'em in here. How I wish I had some right now. I'm starved!

CLARENCE (*Doubtfully*): Well, it's true we take litronium internally—

ANDY: Bob, litronium might be the same thing as hot dogs!

BOB: Yeah! Say, maybe Howard has some in the refrigerator. I'll go see! (*He runs out eagerly.*)

ANDY (*To* CLARENCE): He'll be right back.

CLARENCE (*Wearily*): I—certainly—hope so. All this talking has further exhausted my litronium supply. I'm getting—hermoplated.

ANDY: Hermoplated? What's that?

CLARENCE: In your language it means—pooped, I believe.

At least—that's what—they call it—in the Men from
Earth—Comic Books. (*He staggers to chair and falls
into it.*)

ANDY: Gosh, that's too bad. We just have to get you some
litronium quick! Oh, here comes Bob back with Howard, the professor's cook. (*Enter* BOB *and* HOWARD. BOB
carries hot dogs.)

HOWARD (*Staring at* CLARENCE): Well, I must say you're a
strange one! I suppose you're from Hollywood.

CLARENCE: No, I'm from Clarion.

HOWARD: Clarion . . . Clarion. Let's see, isn't that near
Chicago? My, you're a long way from home, aren't you,
sonny?

BOB: If you only knew, Howard!

HOWARD: You look all worn out. That's a long trip.

CLARENCE: What a strange earth character! (*Turns to*
BOB) Did you bring the litronium, earth boy?

HOWARD: Young man, watch your language. The professor
is very particular.

BOB (*Handing* CLARENCE *hot dog*): Try one of these.

CLARENCE (*Taking it gingerly*): Is this—a hot dog? It—
doesn't look—very much—like litronium. (*Brightens*)
But maybe it's inside the skin. (*Breaks it open and looks
inside*) No, there's no litronium in here.

BOB: Gee, I'm sorry. Do—do you feel as bad as you look?

CLARENCE (*Groaning*): Much worse!

BOB: Andy, go get my uncle and his secretary from his
office. Maybe the professor can figure out what to do.
He's a brain.

ANDY: Okay. (*Snatches up wiener to munch on way out*)
Mm. (*Exits*)

BOB: What about the meteor heading toward earth, Catastrophe Clarence? What are we going to do?

HOWARD: Oh, is your name Clarence, young man? I had a brother named Clarence, or was it a sister named Clara? Isn't that funny, I can't quite remember, it was so long ago, but I know he had long, yellow curls. (*Exists shaking head*)

CLARENCE (*Despairingly*): The meteor will crash into the earth and destroy it in just fifteen minutes if I can't get back up there some way to steer it out of danger. (*Groans*) My first big assignment since I got out of training school—and I'm failing at it! (*Enter* PROFESSOR CLARK *with* GLENN MATTHEWS)

PROFESSOR: Bob, what's all this about? Your friend Andy claims we're entertaining a visitor from outer space. Ridiculous! Nothing but the very lowest forms of life exist on other planets. Atmospheric conditions just won't support evolution there, you know. What kind of joke is this, anyway? (*Looks sternly at* CLARENCE *in chair*)

CLARENCE (*Tries to rise but falls back weakly*): Sir, I am not a low form of life! And I can prove I'm from space. Let me introduce myself. I'm Catastrophe Clarence from the planet, Clarion, on the other side of the moon —and a member of the Universal Meteor Patrol. I had to land here because I ran out of litronium.

PROFESSOR: I can't believe it. I never heard of Clarion or the Universal Meteor Patrol or—or litronium, whatever that is.

BOB: Honest, Uncle Wadsworth, I'm sure he's telling the truth. Andy and I saw the meteor right in your telescope over there. (*Turns to* ANDY) I'm sure that red thing we saw must have been a meteor, Andy!

ANDY: Sure, that's it! It must have been! (*Runs to telescope to look through it*) Yes, there it is—and now it's as big as an orange!

PROFESSOR: Here. Let me look. (*He strides to telescope. His secretary,* GLENN MATTHEWS, *follows*) It's there! The meteor! And it's growing larger every second, too. I can't believe my eyes. I've never seen one that size before. It looks as if nothing could stop it from hitting the earth! Glenn!

GLENN: Yes, professor?

PROFESSOR: Notify the proper authorities. Make my will. Lock all the doors and windows. No, on second thought, leave them open. And tell Howard not to bother about dinner. We probably won't have time to eat it.

GLENN: Heavens, sir! Is it that bad?

PROFESSOR: Take a look for yourself.

GLENN (*Doing so*): Jumping Jupiter! Yes! It's terrible! (*Rushes out of room*) I'll call Washington, notify the newspapers, get in touch with Palomar, call my mother —(*Exits*)

PROFESSOR (*Peers into telescope again*): I can't believe it! It can't be happening! (*Enter* HOWARD *from right.*)

HOWARD: Oh, there you are, professor! I can't remember how you wanted your eggs this morning.

PROFESSOR: Never mind that now, Howard. We won't be eating—

CLARENCE (*Despairingly*): Are you sure you don't have any litronium around here?

BOB: I don't know. There might be, I suppose, if we only knew what it was. What color is it, anyhow?

CLARENCE (*With longing*): It's the—most beautiful— color in—the universe, a soft delicate tender shade—

ANDY: Come on, we're wasting time, and there isn't much of it left! Let's all go out into the kitchen and see what we can find there. Come on, Clarence!

CLARENCE (*Tries to rise but falls back helplessly*): Can't—

stand up. Too—weak. Almost—out of—litronium. Must get some—soon. Meteor will crash—in just—twelve minutes. My—responsibility. Must—save earth.

BOB: I'll stay here. The rest of you go. And hurry! (*They go out.* BOB *goes to* CLARENCE) Don't worry, Clarence. I'm sure they'll find some litronium for you. They just have to!

CLARENCE: I—hope—so. Earth is such—an interesting—planet. Such—crazy—people. My—duty—to save—earth.

BOB: You will. Don't worry. See, here come the others with all kinds of food. See? (*Enter the* PROFESSOR, HOWARD, ANDY *and* GLENN *carrying an assortment of sacks, cartons, milk, salt and other edibles.* HOWARD *carries carton of eggs and box of corn flakes.*)

HOWARD: But I still don't understand what this is all about. Why are we moving everything out of the kitchen into the observatory, professor? This is quite upsetting.

BOB: Poor Catastrophe Clarence! He feels awful. Quick, let's see if any of the stuff you brought is litronium. Gee, I hope it is!

PROFESSOR (*Looking out rear window*): That meteor is almost as big as the sun now—

ANDY: Only it's even redder.

GLENN: And see how light it's getting outside—and quite warm, too!

BOB: Here, space man. (*Holds out slice of whole-wheat bread*) Is this your litronium?

CLARENCE (*Shaking head feebly*): No, not—litronium. Oh, dear!

ANDY: Then how about this? (*Offers milk.* CLARENCE *looks interested at first, but sniffs at it and shakes head.*)

PROFESSOR: Perhaps this is litronium? (*Offers corn flakes, but* CLARENCE *shakes head hopelessly*)

BOB: How about this? It tastes real good. (*Offers root beer*)

CLARENCE: No. No—not that.

ANDY: Then what about this chocolate ice cream? Come on, try some!

GLENN: Try some of these nice California prunes—or some of these figs. They're full of vitamins.

CLARENCE (*Sadly*): Not—litronium.

BOB: Gee, looks like none of this stuff is litronium. What'll we do? That meteor's getting closer and closer and hotter and hotter every minute. (*Wipes brow*) Whew! It feels like Palm Springs on the Fourth of July!

HOWARD: Well, if everyone has finished playing this crazy parlor game, I'll just take everything back to the kitchen where it belongs. I want to get on with breakfast. Great Jumping Jupiter, but it's getting warm! (*Fans self with box of corn flakes.*) Looks like it's going to be a real scorcher today, all right. (*Starts loading up with supplies to take back to kitchen*)

CLARENCE: Just—three minutes—left! Sorry—earth people. I've—failed!

PROFESSOR: Er—before it's too late—ah, Mr. Catastrophe —I feel I owe you an apology for referring to you, as an inhabitant of another planet, as a—a low form of life. Forgive me, sir.

CLARENCE (*Waving hand feebly*): It's—all right. I—understand.

HOWARD (*Noticing jar of smog on table beside milk and picking it up*): Now, what's this? What's this dirty jar doing here? (*Unscrews top curiously*) Yes, it's empty, just as I thought!

BOB: Oh, it's just a jar of smog Andy and I brought from L. A., Howard. Good old Los Angeles smog! I'm going to miss it.

ANDY: Me, too! Just thinking about it makes me choke up.

CLARENCE (*Takes deep breath and sits up*): Litronium! I smell litronium. Where is it? (*Sniffs eagerly*) Oh, it's coming from that jar! Quick, let me have it! (*Snatches jar from bewildered* HOWARD) Ah, thank the planetary powers—litronium at last!

PROFESSOR: You mean to say that smog is—litronium?

CLARENCE (*Inhaling deeply*): Yes, sir! Richest blend I've ever inhaled. Ah—dee-licious! Better than anything available on Clarion or anywhere in outer space.

BOB: You mean—you're going to be all right now?

CLARENCE: Yep. This'll do it. This'll fix me up fine, earth boy. Quick, earth friends, let me out of here! There may still be time to avert disaster. (*Heads for rear window, running and jumping with increasing energy, still carrying jar of smog from which he inhales deeply*) Here I go! Goodbye, earth friends! Thanks for the litronium! I hope I'm not too late to save your planet. One minute to go!

BOB: Goodbye, Clarence—goodbye! Good luck!

ANDY: Gee, I sure hope he gets to that meteor in time! It must be awfully close to earth now. (*Everyone follows* CLARENCE *to window and looks after him.*)

PROFESSOR (*Astonished*): Why, he was out of sight in just one long jump! Never saw anything like it! (*Withdraws head from window, shaking it incredulously*) Remarkable fellow! Highly evolved. This changes everything.

GLENN (*Shouting excitedly*): The meteor's heading west— toward the Pacific Ocean and—and it's getting smaller!

HOWARD (*Crossing room, loaded with supplies*): Great heavens, it seems to be getting darker—much darker. Must be clouding up again. Perhaps hot cakes would be better for breakfast than cold cereal. Whoops! (*Loses some packages, retrieves them*)

BOB: Hurray! Catastrophe Clarence has steered the meteor away from earth! (*Thumps* ANDY *on back excitedly*)

ANDY: Hurray for Clarence! Hurray for smog! (*Thumps* BOB *back*)

PROFESSOR (*Solemnly*): Well, as the old saying goes, one man's meat is another man's poison—and vice versa.

ANDY: What?

BOB: Oh, I get it. You mean that what's smog for some people is litronium for others, huh?

PROFESSOR: Something like that, Bob.

ANDY: Hey! Wait until the Los Angeles Chamber of Commerce hears about this!

BOB: And L.A. isn't the only city in the world with smog. There's St. Louis and London and—and Detroit and lots of others. All big cities have some of it sometimes. And now, just think, smog has saved the whole earth from destruction—and space men need it to live on!

ANDY: Well, I'm glad I don't have to. Say, I'm starved!

BOB: So'm I. How about something to eat, Howard?

HOWARD (*Still dropping and picking up packages*): Just as—as soon as the professor tells me how he wants his eggs this morning.

PROFESSOR (*Shrugging*): Scrambled, Howard—scrambled!

ANDY (*Grinning at* BOB): Well, it looks as if Howard is still in a smog!

THE END

John Crown's Legacy

by Ernst H. Suerken

Characters

JOHN CITIZEN	JOHNNY APPLESEED
JOHN CROWN	HORACE MANN
STEPHEN DAYE	STEPHEN FOSTER
JOHN HANCOCK	CYRUS MCCORMICK
ASHER BENJAMIN	CASEY JONES
ROBERT MORRIS	DR. MORTON
GEORGE WASHINGTON	THE AMERICAN SALESMAN
JOHN PAUL JONES	ROBERT E. PEARY
ELI WHITNEY	LUTHER BURBANK
NOAH WEBSTER	FRANK WOOLWORTH
NAT BOWDITCH	GEORGE W. GOETHALS
DONALD MCKAY	THOMAS ALVA EDISON
CYRUS FIELD	HENRY FORD

SETTING: *The stage is bare. A projector light is thrown on the upstage wall but projects no picture.*

AT RISE: JOHN CITIZEN, *in the role of a narrator, comes forward to speak.*

JOHN CITIZEN: In 1946 a young veteran in Halloran General Hospital wrote a letter to the *New York Times.*

He wrote the letter because he was suffering and because he was anguished. After four years of struggle, the writer of the letter, John Crown, died.

John Crown's legacy to the world was an example of courage and a philosophy of life which, in these troubled and uncertain days, pleads even more eloquently for the necessity of understanding than the day on which his letter was written. In this era of precocious technology, hydrogen bombs, guided missiles and all the additions to the horrors of war that have caused an epidemic of anxiety and tension throughout the world, this pain-racked boy's prescription for peace among men merits thoughtful consideration. (JOHN CITIZEN *returns to one side as* JOHN CROWN *enters in a wheelchair and slowly makes his way to the center of the stage.*)

JOHN CROWN: My name is John Crown. I am a paraplegic at Halloran General Hospital. My physical wounds are very small in comparison with my spiritual wounds. I have come back from death to a world that I no longer care for. I, who have been engaged in the great struggle to save the world from tyranny and have seen my comrades die for this cause, can now find no peace in the world or in my country. Because I lived close to death for two years, the reasons why there is no peace seem infinitesimally flimsy. Russia wants the Dardanelles, Yugoslavia wants Trieste, the Moslems want India, labor wants more wages, capital wants more profit, Smith wants to pass the car in front of him, Junior wants more spending money. To these, I say, is it necessary to kill and cripple human beings for these petty gains? Anyone who thinks a human body is so cheap that it can be traded for a tract of land, a piece of silver, or a few minutes of time should be forced to listen to the moans of the dying, night and day for the rest of his life. All the troubles of the world originate in the common man. The selfish and greedy ways of nations are just the ways of each individual man multiplied a hundredfold. When the morals of the common man drop, so do the morals of the nation and of the world.

As long as our individual morals remain at a low ebb, so will be the world. Until each of us stops "hogging the road" with his car, stops fighting over the seat in the bus, stops arguing over who is to cut the grass, there will be no peace in the world. If man wishes peace again, he must return to the great Commandment, "Love thy neighbor as thyself for the love of God."

JOHN CITIZEN (*Comes forward and approaches the seated* JOHN CROWN *in his wheelchair. Picture of Paul Revere's Ride is projected*): You answered your country's call, John Crown, and deserve well of her. But there were others in other times and places who suffered and fought through troubled times that you who are a part of their posterity might enjoy our American heritage. There were those who answered the call to arms of Paul Revere at midnight—April 18, 1775—as he roused the farmers to meet on Lexington Green with their long muskets and molded bullets. They fired their shots for freedom and independence too. (JOHN CROWN *drowses as we follow his dream.* JOHN CITIZEN *pushes the wheelchair to such a position that it will not interfere with the projection from the opaque projector.*

JOHN CITIZEN *also brings himself a comfortable chair and seats himself in such a manner that it does not interfere with the projection.*)

STEPHEN DAYE (*Comes on stage as picture of* STEPHEN DAYE *or a printer operating a wooden press is placed on screen*): John Crown, listen to me. My name is Stephen Daye and I came to these shores not too long after the *Mayflower.* I brought my types and my wooden presses that made it possible to speak to all people. There were others who came after me. Ben Franklin and his newspaper—Bobbie Bell who printed Tom Paine's *Common Sense*—at the risk of his life. We fought for freedom too—freedom of the press and we are proud of the legacy we left you—a press that is the voice of a free people. (*He exits. Picture of Boston Tea Party projected.*)

JOHN CITIZEN (*Leans forward in his chair half-rising and addresses* JOHN CROWN *earnestly*): John Crown, do you remember studying about the Boston Tea Party in school? The men who held that tea party brewed their independence in the world's biggest teapot—Boston Harbor. (*Music—"Yankee Doodle"*) They tossed the tea with its unwanted tax over the sides into the harbor depths. They proved to an English King that they were free and independent men who would not be dictated to from across an ocean. (*Sits back in his chair. Picture of the signing of the Declaration of Independence is projected.* JOHN HANCOCK *enters with a swagger, carrying a large goose quill pen with a flourish for all to see.*)

JOHN HANCOCK: When I signed my name to a document— the Declaration of Independence—I signed it for all to see. Even today you talk of a signature as being your

John Hancock. I signed the Declaration of Independence because I knew that it was right and that our independence was basic to all else if our freedom was to grow. (*Exits. Picture of a house being built in colonial times projected.*)

ASHER BENJAMIN (*Enters carrying a copy of the book which he has written and moves about the stage as he speaks, pointing out the foundation, fireplaces, doorway, fanlight or whatever the particular picture offers*): I never wore a soldier's uniform. I never fought a battle. But I did write a book—this book, *The Country Builder's Assistant,* by Asher Benjamin. It told the people how to build a house or a church. The carpenter, the farmer and others could read about foundations, fireplaces, doorways and fanlights. I am proud that my book helped many a man to build his house and his church where he was free to live and free to worship. (*Exits. Picture of* ROBERT MORRIS *pleading for more money is projected.*)

ROBERT MORRIS (*Enters with a serious look and carries a money bag which is almost empty*): I am no soldier and have no taste for uniforms and their trappings, but I fought in our first war for freedom too. My name is Robert Morris and it was my job to pay the Continental Army's bills. We had no cash. We had no credit, but we had to have money. I used my own. I borrowed. I begged, I asked, I cajoled. And somehow we always found enough to keep the fight for freedom going. When there was no money left, I had to make my own, backed only by my promise to pay. Fortunately, there were those who believed in me—so you see freedom is still worth fighting for—because we wrested it out of adversity before. (*Exits slowly. Picture of* GEORGE WASH-

INGTON *at Mount Vernon, or a picture of Mount Vernon alone.*)

GEORGE WASHINGTON (*Enters and addresses his speech with great earnestness to both* JOHN CROWN *and the audience*): You should know, John Crown, that six years of war is enough to weary any man. When the war was over, I wanted only to return to Virginia. (*Music— "Carry Me Back to Ole Virginny"*) But the people of the United States said otherwise. They asked me to be their President and who was I to say no? That was how I came to be the first President of the United States of America—a new country where the people governed and the Chief Executive worked for all the people—a free and independent people. (*Exits. Picture of* JOHN PAUL JONES *on a frigate in full sail, or other appropriate naval picture.*)

JOHN PAUL JONES (*Comes in with a rather truculent air and plants himself with feet apart as if on the rolling deck of a ship. Speaks with the crisp manner of a man accustomed to command*): It wasn't only the soldiers who fought for freedom. My name is an ordinary name: Jones—John Paul Jones to be exact. I went to sea as a boy of twelve and I was booted about by tyrannical ship captains. I never liked tyranny, and independence came to be my ideal. I fought for that ideal with an old ship that served me as a man o'war. We had men of iron and ships of wood whose guns fought for freedom. That was how our Navy was born. (*Exits. Music— "Blow the Man Down." Picture of the cotton gin or* ELI WHITNEY, *or both, is projected.*)

ELI WHITNEY (*Enters carrying a spool from which small nails protrude and a small crank with which he tinkers as he speaks*): A new country does not grow up full-blown overnight. It takes time to put one's house in order. It isn't always possible to manufacture things in the beginning. When I was a boy we used both foreign guns and foreign cloth in this country. I wanted to help my country become economically independent. I tinkered. Out of my tinkering came the cotton gin. I, Eli Whitney, was an inventor. After the cotton gin came more tinkering. A free country needs not only soldiers and sailors, but farmers, financiers, printers and inventors. (*Exits. Picture of old-time school with slates, and schoolmaster in charge.*)

NOAH WEBSTER (*Enters with a blue-backed book which he uses as his Blue-Backed Speller through which he leafs as he speaks*): There is something else we Americans have learned to value. Education didn't amount to much when I went to school. I found it dull and dreary and I, Noah Webster, decided to do something about it so that learning would be more interesting. I wrote a speller called *The Blue Backed Speller*. It was the first of its kind and here it is. I tried to make it more than a speller by putting interesting things into the book. The boys and girls of America liked my *Speller* so much that it came to be used throughout the country. We had something in America that could not be found elsewhere; our children were free to learn if they wanted to. (*Exits. Picture of a navigator taking a bearing—shooting the sun—or similar picture*)

NAT BOWDITCH (*Enters with the rolling gait of a sailor. If possible, he should carry a sextant with which he sights. Lacking this he should have a spy glass*): My name is Nat Bowditch and I hail from Salem, Massachusetts. I grew up to be a sailing master, as many a Salem man did. I studied the stars, the tides and the ways of the sea. I also read all the books on navigation and was amazed to find any number of fool mistakes in the best of them. Their fool mistakes made me so mad I wrote the *New American Practical Navigator* so American seafaring men would no longer have to sail their ships in ignorance. (*Remains on stage as* DONALD McKAY *enters holding a ship model which he handles admiringly. Project a picture of a graceful clipper ship.*) You must be Donald McKay, the man who made American clipper ships famous.

DONALD McKAY: I learned to build ships in a New England shipyard. I learned to love building ships and perhaps they performed so well because I had faith in the ships I built. They were known as clipper ships and I was proud that clipper ships built by Donald McKay out of oak and pine were bigger and faster than the ships before them. I was proud that they carried the free and independent American flag to every port in the world. (BOWDITCH *and* McKAY *exit, singing "Haul Away, Joe," a sea chanty. Appropriate picture of Stormalong, or scene of a storm or a dead calm at sea is projected.*)

JOHN CITIZEN (*Moves forward to the center of the stage*): As the country grew so did its folklore. I want to tell you a little about Stormalong. He was the Paul Bunyan of the sea about whom the seafaring men spun their yarns. There was nothing in and out of the water that Stormalong didn't have his hand in. Stormalong helped Columbus. Stormalong was with the *Mayflower* and with John Paul Jones when he started the United States Navy. He helped build the Panama Canal and made the white cliffs of Dover. Stormalong still travels with American seafaring men wherever they may go. (*Goes back to his seat. Picture of a ship laying cable is projected.*)

CYRUS FIELD (*Enters giving the impression of the well-dressed, affluent man who has made his mark and who is a little impatient with things*): They told me that it was impossible and that irked me, as it has many another American. I, Cyrus Field, thought my life had been full enough and I planned to take it easy. But the idea of laying a cable across the Atlantic Ocean challenged me so I couldn't rest until I tried, because they said it couldn't be done. The first cable extended three hundred and sixty miles out before it broke. The ocean won the second round. On the third try the cable waited until we had gone twelve hundred miles before it parted. We tried again and on the fourth try we won— the cable was laid and messages could be sent across the ocean. I had shown that the impossible was possible and that nothing is impossible. (*Exits triumphantly. Picture of apple tree, or apple orchard in full blossom, or one of* JOHNNY APPLESEED.)

JOHNNY APPLESEED (*Enters with a bag over his shoulder from which he scatters seeds on the stage as he speaks*): My name—that is my baptismal name, is Jonathan Chapman and I am a plain and humble man but I am happy that my name has come down through the years as Johnny Appleseed. You ask why? I'll tell you why. I loved trees—especially apple trees. Perhaps that is why they grew so splendidly. Wherever I went up and down the land I planted trees, apple trees. There came a night when I went to sleep under an apple tree and did not wake up because my mission was accomplished, but my trees have lived on. (*Exits. Picture of* STEPHEN FOSTER *at the piano projected.*)

STEPHEN FOSTER (*Comes on stage and goes to the center of the stage speaking. If character has a good singing voice, he sings "Jeannie with the Light Brown Hair"*): When I was a boy someone told me that the man who really mattered was the man who wrote a nation's songs. I never forgot that. I was not like other boys. While they were busy with their games and treasures, I listened to the sounds of everything about me and later I wove them into songs—folk songs of the nation which have become a part of our common heritage. You know my songs: Sewanee River, My Old Kentucky Home, Old Black Joe and Jeannie with the Light Brown Hair—by Stephen Foster. (*Exits singing. Music —"Jeannie with the Light Brown Hair." Picture of an early reaper or wheat field projected.*)

CYRUS McCORMICK (*Enters dressed as a farmer and speaks with a farmer's drawl*): It has taken all sorts of men to make this nation. The backbone of the country has always been its farmers who tilled the soil and fed the nation. I, Cyrus McCormick, was a farmer's son and I had a dream that would lighten their burden. My dream was that a farmer should be able to cultivate more than a few paltry acres. It took me a long time to hammer out my dream in the shop. I didn't know whether or not the contraption was going to work. It did work and a new piece of farm equipment came into being—the reaper—a machine that could reap thirty acres of wheat. I had made my dream come true and the American farmer's life was an easier and a more abundant one. (*Exits. Picture of a locomotive being driven, or other appropriate picture in railroading if no picture of* CASEY JONES *can be found.*)

CASEY JONES (*Enters dressed as a railroad engineer wear-*

ing an engineer's cap and gauntlet gloves in his hands which he draws on as he speaks): The railroads helped make America great and wherever railroad men gather they talk about "Casey" Jones. I was baptized John Luther Jones but folks just naturally called me "Casey." My hometown was Cayce, Kentucky, and maybe that had something to do with it. I was a railroad engineer and I would rather drive a locomotive than eat. I loved that engine. Maybe it was because of this that I could get things out of my engine that no other engineer could. I drove my train till one night when there was a freight train in the way. There was a song about me and my train which I left behind for you to hear and catch the spirit of railroad men like "Casey" Jones. Listen! (*Exits. Music—"Casey Jones." Picture of an old-time operation.*)

DR. MORTON (*Enters in frock coat carrying an ether syringe which he holds in front of him as he speaks*): Americans are always looking for something. I, Dr. William Morton, dentist, was looking for a way to give my fellow-Americans freedom from pain. I had a hunch that ether could give relief from pain and after much experimenting I was sure that I was right. When the time came, physicians gave me a chance to prove my ether. When the patient slept after the ether was administered, as the operation progressed free from pain, my happiness knew no bounds. (*Exits. Picture of Pecos Bill projected.*)

JOHN CITIZEN (*Moves forward on stage addressing* JOHN CROWN): Every part of this country has contributed to its folklore and the West was no exception for the West gave us Pecos Bill. Bill was tough because he had been brought up by a coyote and taught by a grizzly bear. Bill invented everything that had to do with the cattle range. Roping was his idea and with one throw of his lariat he could loop a whole herd of cattle. He dug the Rio Grande one morning so there would be water for his private range. He was a rootin', tootin' dream come true, but one day he met a dude all dressed up who asked so many questions Bill just lay down and laughed himself to death. (*Goes back to his chair. Music—"Red River Valley" or "Green Grow the Lilacs." Picture of a peddler and his wagon projected.*)

THE AMERICAN SALESMAN (*A rather dapper character enters*): You don't know who I am because I have no particular name. I am he who helped to civilize this country by making more things available to more people. I went my rounds on muleback, dodging Indians between my calls. Then I was a peddler making my rounds with a rickety wagon carrying axes for the farmers and dress goods for the wives and encyclopedias for ambitious youth. Then I was called a drummer as I traveled over the breadth of the land and today you know me as the salesman who sells tractors, radios, iceboxes, movies and all the things Americans are free to enjoy. (*Exits. Picture of the frozen North or* ROBERT E. PEARY *at the North Pole.*)

ROBERT E. PEARY (*Enters dressed for cold weather from head to foot with a parka and hood*): I am Robert E. Peary. I spent my life looking for the North Pole—for the place where there is no more North—the top of the world. I made many trips before I reached my goal and each one taught me more about how to live in the barren North. The Arctic fought me every inch of the way. My feet were frozen. My toes were amputated. I learned to eat dog and I tasted failure. But I had to make that last attempt by ship and sledge which brought us to our goal—the North Pole. (*Exits. Picture of a woman who will serve to epitomize the American Woman is projected.*)

JOHN CITIZEN (*Comes forward to center of stage*): These are the men who have told you of their part in building this nation's heritage. There have been great men in that heritage, but we must not lose sight of the women who helped these men become great. They shared their lives with the pioneers and the others. Hers was the gentle voice in time of trouble. She reassured her children and buoyed up her man when he thought he had failed. She had the quiet courage to try again when the money was gone and the crops had failed. She is the epitome of all the women who have made this country great by making a home for her man and her children. (*Returns to his chair. Picture of* LUTHER BURBANK *puttering in his garden or a picture of flowering garden or orchard is projected.*)

LUTHER BURBANK (*Enters, dressed for work in a garden with a wide-brimmed hat on the back of his head. He carries a green plant in his hands and a grafting knife with which he works as he talks*): I spent my life talking gently to Nature and finding out her secrets for the benefit of man. I tended my garden carefully and puttered with plants for fifty years. During those fifty years I learned from Nature how to create plants. I found out how to grow larger and whiter potatoes. I made it possible for cattle to eat cactus and for strawberries to ripen all the year. Luther Burbank's legacy to America, to you and the world, was to leave the good earth covered with flowers and fruits that had never grown before. (*Exits. A succession of pictures should be used with this: (1) Picture of* HORACE MANN *pleading the cause of public education. (2) A one-room school. (3) Pictures of modern schools in rapid succession. All projected as* HORACE MANN *speaks.)*

HORACE MANN (*Enters*): I was born a long time ago, before there were any public schools in this country of ours, with a great hunger. My hunger for knowledge was greater than my hunger for food. I borrowed books and I searched for knowledge wherever I could. I read law which was the way you became a lawyer in those days. Most lawyers were politicians and I was no exception. I, Horace Mann, became President of the Massachusetts Senate. It was suggested that someone should look into and report on school conditions in the Commonwealth of Massachusetts. The job was a poor one, but I knew what I had to do. It was not to be a lawyer, senator or politician, but to plead the cause of America's children and fight for their right to learn. And fight I did until there were schools throughout the land—public schools for all—not just for the few. And the message I left for America still holds true today: "Be afraid to die until you have done something for humanity." (*Exits. A picture of a red-fronted five-and-dime store or the interior of a five-and-ten is projected.*)

FRANK WOOLWORTH (*A substantial character—a typical storekeeper who enters and expansively tells the story of his store*): I had an American dream too. My dream was of a new kind of store where things would cost only a nickel or a dime. This was my kind of store because I knew from experience that most Americans had only nickels and dimes left to spend after their family bills were paid. You know it as the five-and-ten, where you can buy an endless variety of things, but the first dime store was one you could walk into and buy anything you saw for no more than a dime. I wanted my store to be gay, so I painted it red, and people came to Frank Woolworth's little store and bought happiness for their nickels and dimes. (*Exits. Picture of* PAUL BUNYAN *projected.*)

JOHN CITIZEN (*Comes forward to center of stage*): There's still another to join the company of Stormalong and Pecos Bill. His name is Paul Bunyan, who stood a mile high and used a pine tree for a comb. A sweep of his arm and there was lumber enough for a dozen houses. He could lay a hundred miles of railroad ties or make paper books by the thousands. Paul Bunyan was the giant that built this country with every woodsman's axe that ever felled a tree. (*Returns to chair. Picture of the Panama Canal—before and after—is projected, if possible.*)

GEORGE W. GOETHALS (*Enters dressed in whites, with a pith helmet, carrying a roll of blueprints which he unrolls and consults as he talks*): America needed a canal. It was to be a canal that would join the Atlantic and Pacific oceans. The place for it was the Isthmus of Panama. A Frenchman named DeLesseps had tried and failed, leaving nothing but a big ditch. America wanted a canal and they asked me, George Washington Goethals, to finish the big ditch and make it into a canal. It was a mess. There was fever to combat. Workers to be housed and fed. A railroad to be built. A mountain to be split and a river to be dammed. We did them all with an army of sixty-five thousand workers. The Panama Canal was built and the oceans flowed together. (*Exits. Picture of* EDISON *as a young man studying.*)

THOMAS ALVA EDISON (*He carries a valise or box, from*

which he takes a toy telegraph key, an electric light bulb, a toy phonograph and a toy motion picture projector as he talks): When I was a boy I was just young Tom Edison to the neighbors and they said I couldn't leave well enough alone. That was my trouble. I was always meddling with things. If there were better ways of doing things I wanted to know how. They said that only one telegraph message could go over a wire; I showed them how to send two messages over the same wire. The telegraph could send fifty words a minute; the fifty became a thousand. I dreamed of a better light than gas and successfully put electricity into the incandescent lamps which glow in homes all over the world. My meddling brought about the phonograph that talks and sings, and moving pictures were my brain child. It was a good thing, don't you think, that I couldn't leave well enough alone? (*Exits. Picture of the first Ford or* HENRY FORD *working on his first car in the shop, or a series of pictures of the first cars are projected in succession.*)

HENRY FORD (*Enters dressed in a mechanic's apron, carrying a wrench*): You take automobiles for granted. It wasn't too many years ago that there weren't any automobiles. They called them horseless carriages in the beginning and thought that they were only for fools. But I, Henry Ford, had a vision. The car I would build would bring transportation within the reach of all. Transportation to work, to market, to school, to wherever people wanted to go. There would be roads and Americans would be neighbors. These were the ideas I built in the first machine I put together with my own hands in the little shop on Bagley Avenue. That first machine has become millions and the making of automobiles a basic American industry which contributes to our American way of life. (*Picture of a steel mill or blast furnace in full operation.*)

JOHN CITIZEN (*Comes forward to center of stage*): Do you know a man named Joe Magarac? Of course you don't, because he belongs with Stormalong, Pecos Bill and Paul Bunyan. Joe can dip up steel and roll it in his hands. Joe can squeeze out miles of shining steel tracks. Joe can shape up cannon balls like mud pies and flatten ingots like you roll pie crust. Joe cuts up the sheets with his teeth. Joe Magarac's mighty steel muscles are how we got this country made. (*Returns to his chair. Picture of Casey at the Bat projected.*) They call baseball the national pastime. Sure it's as American as apple pie. I want to tell you about two men in baseball. Did you ever hear about Casey at the Bat? There was the time when he let two go by and whiffed the third. He was the world's biggest bum because the mighty Casey had struck out. Still he had three chances at the ball and another chance at bat when the time came. (*Picture of BABE RUTH projected*) Then there was the "Babe"— George Herman Ruth—Babe Ruth, King of Swat, who could hit a ball harder and farther and more often than any other player. The "Babe" had it tough as a kid, but he made the grade. The "Babe" had time for everyone —the newsboy on the corner—the sick kid in the hospital—the big shot—and we loved him for it. He endeared himself to everyone because those of us under forty were "Kid" and those of us over forty were a respectful "Doc." There was one thing in common about "Casey" and the "Babe"—they both showed us how to play the game. (*Pause: appropriate soft music is played. Picture of the Tomb of the Unknown Soldier at*

Arlington is projected. JOHN CITIZEN *rises and pushes* JOHN CROWN'S *wheelchair so that he is looking at the picture.* JOHN CITIZEN *places himself in such a manner that he can see the picture and address* JOHN CROWN *and the audience at the same time.*) John Crown, we know your name and what you've done, and for that we are grateful. But there are countless others who, too, have served in freedom's cause, whose names we'll never know. John Crown, your legacy is greater than you think, so share with me in paying tribute to those whose names we'll never know. We have paid tribute to him as the Unknown Soldier who lies at Arlington. Look! He is a stranger to all of us, yet he is a brother to all of us, for he was a soldier who gave his life in behalf of democratic freedom and he deserves our reverence, not only on Veterans' Day but every day, as we strive to keep his memory green through the corridors of time. (*Music—"Taps." Curtain.*)

THE END

Yellow Fever

by Cora Burlingame

Characters

MAJOR WALTER REED, M.D., *U. S. Army Medical Corps of Cuba and President of the Yellow Fever Board. Handsome, dignified in bearing. There are white streaks in his brown hair.*

MAJOR JAMES CARROLL, *assistant to* DR. REED. *Stocky, of English parentage.*

DR. JESSE LAZEAR, *another member of the Board, he is about* CARROLL'S *age, but younger than* DR. REED. *He is tall, thin, and wears glasses.*

DR. ARISTIDES AGRAMONTE, *the Cuban member of the Board. Small, dark, and middle-aged, he is deliberate in speech and movement.*

WILLIAM DEAN, *a young sergeant in the U. S. Army in Cuba.*

DAN GALLAGHER, *a reporter from the States.*

ARTHUR JANSEN, *an intern.*

DR. ROBERT COOKE.

WARREN JERNEGAN ⎱ *Privates, Hospital Corps.*
LEVI FOLK ⎰

JOHN KISSINGER, *Private, U. S. Army in Cuba.*

JOHN MORAN, *another Private.*

Scene 1

SETTING: *The Office of* DR. WALTER REED *in the Field Hospital of the American Army of Occupation in Cuba, August 1900.*

AT RISE: DR. REED'S *office is a small room with a screened triple window at left of a screened double door in rear wall. A plain oak desk is upstage at left and another downstage at right. There is an army cot under the windows. There is a large cabinet at right of door through the glass doors of which books, pamphlets, and simple laboratory apparatus can be seen. At center down stage is a wooden table on which are a microscope, stoppered flasks, stoppered test tubes in a rack, forceps, scalpel and glass slides. Half a dozen camp chairs are disposed about the room. DR. REED seated at the desk at left is looking over a report. DR. LAZEAR is standing at the table labeling test tubes.*

REED (*Laying down the report*): The Yellow Fever Board, and particularly myself as its president, are under ever-lasting obligations to you, Jesse, for this (*He raps the report with the knuckles of his right hand.*) excellent report on the Carroll-Dean experiment.

LAZEAR (*Smiling, without looking up from his work*): Agramonte had a hand in it.

REED: There is enough credit to go around. (*He takes a sheet of paper out of an official-looking envelope.*) Here is a letter from Washington requesting that we admit an Associated Press reporter to our Yellow Fever Board meeting this morning. (LAZEAR, *registering surprise, places a test tube in the rack.*)

LAZEAR: Publicity at this stage of our investigation? (*He frowns.*)

REED: The families of our men here and the public generally want to know what is being done about yellow fever.

LAZEAR (*Passing his hand wearily over his forehead and eyes*): Of course. So many of our men have died with it.

REED: Too many. (*He touches a white lock on his head.*) That's where these white hairs have come from. That and anxiety over Carroll and Dean.

LAZEAR: And the nursing, sir. You should have left nursing them to us who have less responsibility than you, Dr. Reed.

REED: Night after night when you should have been in your quarters asleep I saw *your* shadow passing back and forth in that pesthouse between Carroll and Dean.

LAZEAR (*Smiling*): You set the example, sir, of not leaving them to the nurses.

REED (*Passionately*): Who could sleep when night after night their fever broke all records? Who could lie in bed when our colleague and a brave soldier were tortured in a hideous battle with death in the interest of humanity and science? (*He makes an obvious attempt to control his emotions.*) Jesse, as a matter of fact, you did a more thorough job of overworking during Dr. Carroll's and Sergeant Dean's attack than any of the rest of us. (LAZEAR *makes a gesture of dissent.* REPORTER *enters the room, fanning himself with a palmleaf fan.*)

LAZEAR: Here's our reporter.

REPORTER: Gallagher's the name, Dan Gallagher of the Associated Press. (*To* REED.) You are Dr. Reed, I presume?

REED: I am Walter Reed, Mr. Gallagher, and this gentleman is Dr. Jesse Lazear, another member of the Yellow Fever Board. (*The men shake hands.*)

REPORTER: I was told at Headquarters that a meeting of the Yellow Fever Board was in session.

REED (*Taking a watch out of his pocket, glances at it*): The other gentlemen are due.

LAZEAR (*Going toward the door.*) Here they are. (DRS. CARROLL *and* AGRAMONTE, *followed by* SERGEANT DEAN, *enter.* REPORTER *lays his fan aside and takes notebook from pocket.*)

REED: Gentlemen, this is Mr. Gallagher, an Associated Press Reporter sent down from Washington to attend this meeting. (CARROLL *and* AGRAMONTE *exchange looks of dismay.* DEAN *grins sheepishly.*) Mr. Gallagher, this (*He lays his hand on* CARROLL'S *arm.*) is my assistant, Dr. James Carroll, and this gentleman (*He motions in the direction of* AGRAMONTE.) is Dr. Aristides Agramonte, both members of the Yellow Fever Board. This good soldier here is Sergeant William Dean. He and Dr. Carroll were the first two volunteers to take the experimental bites of the *aëdes egypti* mosquito, formerly known as *stegomyia fasciata,* which we suspect is the carrier of yellow fever. Gentlemen, be seated. (*All sit.*)

AGRAMONTE: Meaning no offense toward Mr. Gallagher, Dr. Reed, I should like to suggest that publicity at this time might seriously hamper the research being carried on by the Yellow Fever Board.

REED: Every member of the Board feels that way, Dr. Agramonte. Before Mr. Gallagher leaves this room he will be in sympathy with this attitude. But, think of this: as often as three times a week, I have to sign a letter telling some wife or mother in the States that her husband or her son is (*His voice comes near breaking*) dead of yellow fever. All of us have nightmare dreams of the disease becoming epidemic among our soldiers. The families of our men share that dread. The least we can do at this time to lessen this horror is to acquaint the American public with what means we are taking to discover the cause and stop the spread of yellow fever. (*The* REPORTER *writes busily while* DR. REED *is talking.*) Dr. Agramonte, will you, for the benefit of Mr. Gallagher, make brief mention of the distribution of the disease?

AGRAMONTE: As far as I know, the earliest mention of the disease is found in Central America in 1596. It later was heard of among the American Indians in New England. It was epidemic in the West Indies several times during those decades. Later it appeared in New York, in Boston and in Philadelphia. During the last two centuries it has visited seven of the Gulf and Atlantic coastal cities in epidemic form and crept up the Mississippi as far as Memphis. The most devastating invasion of the disease occurred in Philadelphia in 1793.

REED: Thank you, Dr. Agramonte. You have a head for figures, Dr. Lazear. Will you give Mr. Gallagher some idea of the cost in human life of this mysterious disease?

LAZEAR: My data of course are far from complete. But in 1664, on the West Indian island of St. Lucia, yellow fever killed 1,411 people out of a population of 1,500. In the same place 200 out of 500 soldiers died of it in the following year. It is estimated that the death-toll from yellow fever in North America has passed the 100,-000 mark. (*While* LAZEAR *is talking, the* REPORTER *stops twice to wipe his face and wrists.*)

REED: Dr. Carroll, if you feel up to going over briefly what we call our clues to the identity of the cause or the carrier of yellow fever, we'd like to hear from you.

CARROLL: It's you, Dr. Reed, and the other members of the board who have been overworking. I'm up to anything. (*He grins.*) Mr. Gallagher, it appears that in tropical climates persons contract yellow fever the year around. In temperate zones cases occur only in the summer. Epidemics seem to start in low, wet localities or near docks. Persons living in high places occasionally come down with yellow fever; but where investigation has been made, it has been proved that they had recently come from marshy districts or from the vicinity of wharves. The disease seems to spread in the direction of prevailing winds.

REPORTER (*Brightly*): That sounds like mosquitoes! (*His tone and vigor are in sharp contrast to the tired voices and appearance of fatigue or illness showing on the other men.*) In fact, I read in a book while I was coming down on the boat that Dr. Carlos Finlay of Havana announced in 1881 that yellow fever is carried by mosquitoes!

AGRAMONTE: During a half century of experience with yellow fever epidemics in Cuba, Dr. Finlay made observations and came to certain conclusions which we accept tentatively as working hypotheses. But we are no nearer control of yellow fever than we were fifty years ago.

CARROLL: And we are far from proving that mosquitoes are the sole carriers of the disease. It is possible that both Sergeant Dean and myself were infected with yellow fever virus from some other source before we took the bite of the *aëdes egypti*.

REED: Dr. Carroll, may we impose on you further by asking you to say something about your own experience with a severe case of yellow fever?

CARROLL (*Smiling*): There isn't much to tell. *Aëdes egypti* infected with fatal cases of yellow fever fed on my arms. Six days later I came down with the disease. I pulled through because Drs. Reed, Lazear, Agramonte, and Jansen, an intern, fought for my life day and night.

REED: Sergeant Dean, what have you to say about your case of yellow fever?

DEAN (*Obviously embarrassed*): I gave a blood-meal to the same mosquitoes that bit Dr. Carroll four days after they fed on him. In six days the yellow fever got me. We laughed at each other at first because our faces and chests turned the color of brass. Then we quit laughing, and I don't want to say anything more about that, except that these doctors here and the intern wore themselves out looking after me like— (*His chin quivers.*) like my mother did when I was a little kid.

REED (*Rising*): Gentlemen, we all agree that the experiments that will give us the information we need for the control of yellow fever have only begun. Inspired by the heroic examples of Dr. Carroll and Sergeant Dean, we will not lack volunteers. The next subjects will be quarantined twenty-one days before they take the bite of the infected mosquitoes, in the hope of lessening the chances of a prior contagion. Mr. Gallagher, I must ask you at your convenience to go over with me the notes you have taken. This meeting is adjourned.

QUICK CURTAIN

*　　　*　　　*

Scene 2

Setting: *Same as Scene 1. A month later.*

At Rise: Dr. Lazear *is seated at the table looking into a wire mesh insect cage. He stops and rubs his eyes wearily.* Jansen *enters through doors at rear. He crosses the room to the table.* Dr. Lazear *hurriedly puts the cage aside.*

Jansen: It's midnight, Dr. Lazear. (Dr. Lazear *smiles without looking up.*)

Dr. Lazear: Then it's high time you were in bed and asleep, Jansen.

Jansen *(Worried)*: I slept the clock around every day for a week following the recovery of Dr. Carroll and Sergeant Dean. To my certain knowledge, in a month you have not averaged five hours rest in twenty-four. *(Protestingly, even irritated)* Why do you drive yourself so hard, Dr. Lazear? We can't have you working yourself to death! Dr. Reed—the men—need you!

Dr. Lazear *(Eagerly)*: Do you really want to know why I have stayed on the job over-time since the recovery of Dr. Carroll and Sergeant Dean? (*He goes to* Dr. Carroll's *desk.*)

Jansen *(Sternly)*: Nothing can justify a member of the Yellow Fever Board killing himself with work.

Dr. Lazear: I think I've found something out about conditions of infection by yellow fever!

Jansen: You certainly have attended enough men who have sickened and died with yellow fever in the last five weeks to have found out a great deal! (Dr. Lazear *crosses to his own desk, returning with the insect box, and places it on the top of the other desk.*)

DR. LAZEAR (*Enthusiastically*): If I'm right, it's a discovery worth making. From what has happened in the cases I have been observing and timing, it looks as if a mosquito has to bite a yellow fever patient during the first three days of his illness and that the germ or virus has to develop twelve days in the body of the insect before it can be transmitted to a human.

JANSEN (*Indicating the cage*): Is that the mosquito you caught feeding on your orderly who died ten days ago? (*The enthusiasm fades out of* DR. LAZEAR'S *face.*)

DR. LAZEAR (*His voice is low and sad*): It is. (*He places the box on the table.*)

JANSEN (*Attempting to appear casual*): I wish it weren't always a female mosquito that does the biting. (DR. LAZEAR *nods without smiling.*) Let me have a look at her. She is now at her most dangerous stage, isn't she? (DR. LAZEAR *nods again.* JANSEN *leans over the box and peers into it.*) I don't see her.

DR. LAZEAR: Its marking of a silver lyre on its back ought to make it conspicuous against that dark wire mesh. But this light isn't very good. (*He squints up at the light. His eyes follow a mosquito that circles about his head and settles on the back of his left hand resting on the table. He watches it while it feeds.*)

JANSEN (*Still looking into the box.*) Unless I'm blind, there is no mosquito in this box! (*Looks up and sees the mosquito feeding on* DR. LAZEAR'S *hand. He grabs it and holds it in his balled fist.* JANSEN *is angry.*) You deliberately let it out of the box, even though the Yellow Fever Board rejected you as a subject for experimentation because you cannot— (*He presses his lips together and is silent.*)

DR. LAZEAR (*Quietly*): Please—Jansen.

JANSEN (*Excitedly*): Maybe it's a culex—harmless; or an anopheles carrying only malaria! Maybe it isn't an *aëdes egypti*! (*He opens his hand, grabs a small tripod magnifier and looks at the dead mosquito lying in a smear of blood on his palm. Horrified, he lets the magnifier fall. He drops his head and covers his face with his left hand.*) Oh, how could you deliberately let it feed on you! How could you do this to yourself. . . . And to us. . . . (*Voice breaks.*)

DR. LAZEAR (*Setting the cage on the table*): Please place the insect on this sheet of paper, Jansen. Report to your quarters immediately and say nothing of this. (JANSEN *takes up a scalpel and scraping the mosquito off his hand, lays it on a sheet of paper. He goes out, his head lowered. DR. LAZEAR takes up the mosquito with small forceps, places it on a slide, and reaches for the microscope.*)

CURTAIN

*　　　*　　　*

SCENE 3

SETTING: Same as *Scene 1*.

AT RISE: DR. REED *is seated at his desk, opening mail. DR. CARROLL is crossing the room going from his desk to DR. REED's.*

TIME: *Fifteen days later than Scene 2.*

CARROLL: Dr. Agramonte concurs in your opinion that, of the prospective subjects in quarantine, Dr. Robert Cooke and Privates Folk and Jernegan are in condition to make the fomite test. And of the men who have volunteered to undergo the infected mosquito experiments, John Moran and Private Kissinger are the best risks.

REED: I am deeply affected by the splendid morale of our men. I had thought that the tragic death of Dr. Lazear would reduce the number of volunteers.

CARROLL: It seems to have had the opposite effect. (*He lays a bundle of papers on* DR. REED's *desk.*) These are health records of the men who are to make the fomite test. They were made daily while they were in quarantine. We are certain that they have not been bitten by any mosquito within twenty days. (*Enter* COOKE, FOLK, *and* JERNEGAN. *Salutes are exchanged.*)

REED: We are glad to see that you have come through your siege of quarantine looking so fit. (*All the men seat themselves.*) Three of our soldiers died of yellow fever yesterday. Their hospital gowns and their bedclothes are soiled and stiff with their discharges. You are to wear their clothing for twenty-one days and nights, sleeping on the linen of their deathbeds. You will go through this ordeal in a room heated to ninety degrees. The air will be kept moist. There will be no more light than is found in a ship's hold. Night and morning you will shake out the contaminated linen in order to fill the air with the agent of yellow fever, if it is contained in the fomites. Are you still willing to participate in this experiment?

COOKE: We are, sir.

FOLK: Yes, sir.

JERNEGAN: I am willing.

REED: I confess to you gentlemen that the death of my beloved friend and valued colleague, Dr. Jesse Lazear, came near breaking my spirit. It was your request on the day of his funeral, to be allowed to assist in the carrying on of his work that gave me the courage to persist in these experiments, at whatever cost.

COOKE: It seems to me, Dr. Reed, that the memories of Privates Folk and Jernegan might be refreshed by a statement of the results we may expect from the experiment in which we are about to participate. (*Smiling*) That is, of course, if we don't contract yellow fever.

REED: A very good suggestion. Will you state the case?

COOKE: We should keep in mind that there is a widespread belief that airborne fomites from the discharges of yellow fever patients are active agents of the disease. As a result of this belief, millions of dollars' worth of property has been burned during and after each major epidemic of yellow fever—fabrics, priceless works of art, and books that can never be duplicated. Fumigating and sterilizing goods in stores and warehouses have cost firms other millions.

CARROLL: Also, yellow fever patients have often lacked adequate care because nurses and even members of their families have been afraid to touch them or their clothing. (DR. AGRAMONTE *enters and lays a sheet of paper on* DR. REED'S *desk.*)

AGRAMONTE: This is to inform you officially, Dr. Reed, that two hours ago the contaminated clothing and soiled bed-linen were placed in the isolation hut at Camp Lazear. Also, the coal-oil stove was lighted. Temperature of the hut is now ninety degrees Fahrenheit, relative humidity eighty-eight. (COOKE, FOLK, *and* JERNEGAN *spring to their feet, saluting.*)

COOKE: We are ready, Dr. Reed!

REED: Go. And God be with you! (*His voice cracks and his face is distorted under the strain of emotion. He returns the men's salute. With a nod at* DR. REED, AGRAMONTE *leaves, followed by* COOKE, FOLK, *and* JERNEGAN. DR. REED *drops into a chair and sits staring into space.* CARROLL *goes to the window.*)

CARROLL: Here are Moran and Kissinger.

REED (*To himself*): I pray God that we are not sending brave men to their death. (MORAN *and* KISSINGER *enter.* DR. REED *rises to his feet. Salutes are exchanged.*)

MORAN (*Cheerfully*): We are reporting for duty, Dr. Reed!

REED (*Seriously*): I need not remind you gentlemen of the risk involved in the experiment in which you have volunteered to participate. However, it is my duty, officially, to inform you that on the second day of his illness, Dr. Jesse Lazear prevailed on us to allow nine *aëdes egypti* mosquitoes to feed on his arms. Yellow fever virus is now, according to the best of our knowledge, at full strength in these insects. You will give them a full blood meal today. You have been in quarantine long enough for us to assume that you have not previously been infected. Are you risking your lives voluntarily and willingly?

MORAN (*Cheerfully*): Yes, sir. We want to take the bites.

KISSINGER: We both made up our minds to do this the night that Dr. Lazear died. (*A spasm of grief passes over* DR. REED'S *face.*)

REED: I have also to inform you that the Governor of Cuba is offering to all participants in our experiments a bonus of two hundred dollars. If you die of yellow fever, this sum will be paid to your nearest of kin. (MORAN, *smiling, makes a gesture indicating his unwillingness to take the money.*)

KISSINGER: Neither of us will accept the two hundred dollars, sir. We are making the experiment for the sake of humanity and in the interest of science. (DR. REED *draws himself up to his full height and salutes.*)

REED: Gentlemen, I salute you! In my opinion, this exhibition of moral courage has not been surpassed in the annals of the Army of the United States! (CARROLL *salutes.* KISSINGER *and* MORAN, *saluting, leave the room walking briskly, followed by* CARROLL.)

QUICK CURTAIN

* * *

SCENE 4

SETTING: *Same as Scene 1.*

TIME: *Twenty-one days later than Scene 3.*

AT RISE: *Through the door and window it is seen to be dark outside.* DR. REED *walks agitatedly up and down, making nervous movements with his hands.* DR. CARROLL *interrupts his work at his desk to wipe his glasses.*

REED (*Petulantly*): Why didn't I have the common sense to wait until the fomite test came to some sort of an end before the experiments on Moran and Kissinger were begun! (*He beats his fists together behind his back.* DR. CARROLL *looks up and shakes his head despairingly behind* DR. REED's *back. He sighs.*) You! (*He points an accusing finger at* DR. CARROLL.) Why didn't you insist on our concentrating our attention on just one experiment at a time! I'm in my dotage at forty-nine! You're young—still young! (*He drops into a chair and hangs his head dejectedly.*)

CARROLL (*Showing irritation*): How could I—how could anyone have opposed your plan to get at one time, answers to two questions on which hang the life and death of thousands! We knew you were thinking that an epidemic of yellow fever might, any hour, break out in the States, anywhere between Galveston and Boston, and you knew— (*He leans over his desk and speaks slowly, impressively.*) *it could happen here!* All this could have come about and we don't yet know what is the active agent in the spread of yellow fever! We don't know the first principles of sanitation, as far as yellow fever is concerned! (DR. REED *raises his head and wearily passes his hand over his face.*)

REED: I know. . . . I beg you to overlook my manner and what I have said, James. I appreciate your patience and your forbearance. You too must be at the breaking-point. First, we had to lower Jesse Lazear into his grave. Then came the sharp—the unexpected—the unaccountable rise in the yellow fever death rate. Now, at any moment, Agramonte may enter that door and announce that fomites do carry the active agent of yellow fever, which means that we shall have to agonize through another two weeks of Cooke's, Folk's, and Jernegan's sickness, just as we are now being tortured—thinking that word may come at any moment that Moran and Kissinger have died!

CARROLL (*Quietly*): You exhausted your reserve strength many days ago, Dr. Reed. You are now living on hope and faith. We all pray that the suspense will end soon, for your sake. (*Enter* AGRAMONTE, *his face revealing nothing.* REED *and* CARROLL *spring to their feet.*)

REED: Well? (*Exasperated*) Can't you speak, Agramonte?

AGRAMONTE (*Dryly*): Captain Cooke's orderly is standing under a palm tree and by the light of a lantern dousing his superior officer and the two friends with warm soapsuds. They are laughing and scrubbing themselves. (*Instant relief from great anxiety registers on* REED'S *face.*)

REED: Then you are reasonably certain—

AGRAMONTE: I am quite certain that Cooke's, Folk's, and Jernegan's temperatures, pulses, secretions, and skins are normal and that they are in high spirits—not one whit the worse for their gruelling experience.

CARROLL: Which means that there is no danger of infection by contaminated clothing or any other article. We hung that hut full of presumably dangerous objects the day our subjects entered. (*The doors are pulled open and* JANSEN *enters. Seeing* DR. AGRAMONTE, JANSEN *looks startled. Shrinking, he backs toward the door.*)

JANSEN: No! No! They couldn't have gotten yellow fever —not through fomites! Only mosquitoes—o-o-oh. . . . (*Looks from one man to the other.*)

CARROLL (*Soothingly, as a physician speaks to a sick child*): You're right, Jansen. Only mosquitoes carry yellow fever. Dr. Cooke and his friends are dismissed from their experiment in good health. (JANSEN'S *face lights up suddenly.*)

JANSEN (*Voice is shrill from excitement*): Then everything's all right! I'm bringing good news too! The best of news! Mr. Moran and Private Kissinger have no fever! Heart action is normal in both patients!

REED (*Devoutly*): Thank God! That means they will survive the experiment!

JANSEN: During the last two hours they have given unmistakable evidence of recovery. Mr. Moran is hungry! (*He smiles.*)

AGRAMONTE: Dr. Reed, will you give an order for your orderly to pack your kit? Will you go to my place in the hills for a rest that is positively necessary?

REED (*Firmly*): Thank you for your hospitality, Agramonte, but I will not take my leave of absence. To have proof that only mosquitoes carry yellow fever—to learn that Moran and Kissinger are recovering—is all the rest I need. I am refreshed already. (*He actually does seem less weary.*) I cannot rest in the sense that you mean as long as one *aëdes egypti* breeds in a swamp or a coconut shell. This Board will concern itself immediately with the task of destroying all the breeding places of mosquitoes within a radius of ten miles of this site and also of Camp Lazear. We will publish our findings to the world without delay so that it may free itself from mosquitoes and apprehension. Meantime, we will set to work on a series of new experiments using volunteers from among our soldiers as before, in an endeavor to find some means of artificial immunization from attacks of yellow fever. We will labor with redoubled energy because our hearts are light. Our black night of helplessness and despair is past. We know now how to control yellow fever. (*Curtain.*)

THE END

Jiminy Cinders

by Helen Louise Miller

Characters

JIMINY CINDERS, *a would-be cowboy*
BUCKY ⎤
CHUCKY⎬ *his stepbrothers*
LUCKY ⎦
THE GOLDEN RANGER
THE SHERIFF
SLIM ⎤
JIM ⎦ *his deputies*

SCENE 1

SETTING: *Bunkhouse.*

AT RISE: JIMINY CINDERS *is helping his stepbrothers get ready for a rodeo. All are in cowboy costumes except* JIMINY CINDERS.

CHUCKY: Where's my holster? (JIMINY *hands it to him.*)
BUCKY: Get me my gun, boy. (JIMINY *hands it to him.*)
LUCKY: Have you seen my hat? (*Threatening* JIMINY) If you've been trying it on again, I'll larrup you for sure, you Jiminy Cinders.

JIMINY (*Handing* LUCKY *his hat, which he very carefully dusts off*): Oh, no, Lucky, I wouldn't touch your hat.

CHUCKY: You'd better not touch any of our gear, if you know what's good for you.

JIMINY: I never, never do. I never touch anything. Only, please, sometime wouldn't you let me dress up in some of your clothes—just once?

BUCKY (*Laughing*): Did you hear that, Chucky? Why, our duds would just plain drown this little runt!

LUCKY: You'd fall into one of my boots and never get out again.

JIMINY (*With pride*): I'm not as little as all that, and besides, I'll grow.

CHUCKY (*Scornfully*): Oh, sure. You'll grow! You'll grow! Maybe in six or seven years you'll even grow big enough to wear my hatband around your waist for a belt. (*All laugh.*)

BUCKY: Don't stand here talking to this little coot! We've got to get moving if we're to get to that rodeo on time.

JIMINY: Oh, please, won't you take me along?

ALL (*Shouting*): What?

JIMINY (*Ducks in fear, then straightens up and says boldly*): I said, won't you please take me along?

CHUCKY (*With a wink at the others*): Oh, sure, sure, we'll take you along.

JIMINY (*Jumping up and down*): Oh, will you? Will you really?

BUCKY: Sure, kid, why not? Maybe you'd even win the golden spurs.

LUCKY: Come along, Jiminy, and on the way, we'll throw you into the fish pond for bait! (*All laugh uproariously.*)

CHUCKY: You stay where you belong, Jiminy Cinders.

BUCKY: No rodeo for you!

LUCKY: And while we're gone, be sure you clean up this bunkhouse.

CHUCKY: Remember, everything must be shipshape when we get back.

BUCKY: You ride the broom handle for a while instead of a horse, sonny. That's more your speed. (*Exit laughing.*)

JIMINY (*Stamping his foot*): I hate them! I hate them! Some day I'll show them what a cowboy is really like. (*Seizing broom and sweeping wildly*) Sweep, sweep, sweep! That's all I do. I bet if I could go to that old rodeo I'd win the golden spurs. I'd rope a steer so fast they couldn't even count the time! (*Aiming broom at imaginary targets*) I'd draw quicker than any man alive and hit all the bull's-eyes. Bang! Bang! Bang! (*Throws broom on the floor in disgust and drops down on one of the bunks*) But what's the use? They'll never let me go any place. (*Loud pounding on door*) Come in! Come in! (*The* GOLDEN RANGER *enters in complete cowboy outfit. He wears a golden hat, a golden vest, his lariat is a golden rope, and around his waist he wears a golden belt with six golden holsters.*)

RANGER: Howdy, Pardner.

JIMINY: Howdy, Stranger. I don't think we've met.

RANGER: I'm the new Ranger around these parts. I understand your name is Cinders.

JIMINY: Yes, sir, Jiminy Cinders. My stepbrothers aren't at home. They've gone to the rodeo.

RANGER: What about you? Didn't you want to go?

JIMINY: More than anything, but they wouldn't take me. They say I'm too little to be a cowboy.

RANGER: Well, now, I'm right sorry to hear that. How would you like to go along with me?

JIMINY: Do you really mean it?

RANGER: Sure thing. I like company. How about it, Pardner?

JIMINY: Golly! I'd love to go, but I wouldn't dare.

RANGER: Why not? I'd take good care of you.

JIMINY: Because I'm supposed to clean the bunkhouse while they're gone. They make me do all the work . . . even on Rodeo Day.

RANGER: Your stepbrothers sound like a bunch of real varmints, Jiminy.

JIMINY: They think they're going to win the Golden Spurs at the Rodeo, but I bet they're going to have another think coming.

RANGER: How come? Aren't they good cowboys?

JIMINY: Oh, they can ride and shoot and rope a steer, but they're not really cowboys at heart.

RANGER: I think I know what you mean, Jiminy. Now rustle your things together and let's go.

JIMINY: But I don't have any things.

RANGER: You mean you don't have riding boots and a bandanna? Where are your lariat and your cowboy guns?

JIMINY: I don't have any. They say I'm too little to be a cowboy.

RANGER: Well now, Pardner, we'll have to set them straight on that, won't we? Tell you what you do. (*Squatting down in front of* JIMINY) Take off my hat and put it on. (JIMINY *puts on the* RANGER's *hat which falls down around his ears.*) Now, repeat after me:

> I'm a cowboy born, I'm a cowboy bred,
> And I wish this wish inside my head.

JIMINY (*Repeats rhyme as* RANGER *spins the hat around on his head*):

I'm a cowboy born, I'm a cowboy bred,
And I wish this wish inside my head.

RANGER: Now make your wish. Wish for everything a good cowboy needs.

JIMINY (*Still under the hat*):

A cowboy suit and a cowboy hat,
A cowboy gun that can really spat.
A cowboy shirt, and a cowboy rope,
And cowboy boots that will fit, I hope.
And what I wish most, you know, of course,
Is a real cow-punchin' cowboy horse.

RANGER (*Removing hat*): There! That should do it! Now hustle up and I'll wait till you get into your new duds.

JIMINY (*Looking around*): But where are they?

RANGER: Where do you think? Inside your bunk, of course. (JIMINY *pulls back blanket on bunk revealing complete cowboy outfit, minus the holsters and guns. Since he is already wearing blue jeans, he takes only a few seconds to put on the rest of the outfit. The boots are last.*) Sit down there on the bunk, Pardner, and I'll give you a hand with those boots. (*Puts boots on* JIMINY) How do they fit?

JIMINY: Wonderful! Just as if they were made for me.

RANGER: And so they were, Jiminy. They were made just for you. Glad you like 'em. Now for the guns. How would you like these? (*Removes two of his own holsters and fastens them on* JIMINY's *belt.*)

JIMINY: But I can't take these, Ranger. These belong to you.

RANGER: I always make it a point to carry a few spares just in case I meet up with a young fellow like you. (*Adjusting guns*) There now! You look mighty fine.

JIMINY (*Fondling guns admiringly*): But they're gold. I never saw golden holsters and golden guns.

RANGER: You'll notice that your lariat is also gold.

JIMINY: But why? Why is everything made of gold?

RANGER: So you can do golden deeds, Pardner.

JIMINY: Golden deeds?

RANGER: Sure thing. Didn't I tell you I'm known as the Golden Ranger? If we're going to be buddies, you'll have to learn about golden deeds.

JIMINY: Do you think I can learn?

RANGER: I'm sure you can, because I think you've discovered a very wonderful secret. A real cowboy has a heart of gold.

JIMINY: Then my stepbrothers aren't real cowboys, are they?

RANGER: I don't think they are, Jiminy. But we'll find out at the rodeo. Only a real cowboy can win the golden spurs, you know. Now come on, let's hit the saddle.

JIMINY: But I don't have a saddle. I don't even have a horse.

RANGER: Listen! (*Offstage whinny*) Hear that?

JIMINY: Is that your horse, Mister?

RANGER: No, indeed. Goldie has a deeper whinny than that. If I'm any judge of horses, that little feller is waiting for a cowpuncher just about your size.

JIMINY: Then come on, Mister. What are we waiting for? (*Exit.*)

RANGER (*Calling from offstage*): Ride 'em, Cowboy! Hi-ho, Goldie! (*Sound of horses' hoofs growing fainter as curtains close.*)

*   *   *

Scene 2

SETTING: *Same as Scene 1.*

AT RISE: JIMINY CINDERS *is removing his cowboy garments and hiding them in his bunk.* THE RANGER *is talking.*

RANGER: I'm downright proud of you, Pardner. You made a fine showing at the rodeo. You might even have copped off some of the prizes if you hadn't come tearing home in such a doggone hurry.

JIMINY: But I saw my stepbrothers leaving. I had to get here before they discovered I was gone.

RANGER: Still afraid of those varmints, Pardner?

JIMINY: Well, not as much as I was. But I don't want to get 'em all riled up, especially when I've had such a wonderful time. I'll never forget this day, Mister.

RANGER: I'll never forget it either, Jiminy! The way you rode that horse! The way you roped the steers and stuck on those bucking bronchos. Plumb amazing, I call it.

JIMINY: It *was* amazing, Mister. Whenever I swung that golden lariat, I just couldn't miss. And when I gripped those wild ponies and dug my heels in their sides . . . wow! Hey, Mister, look! (*Holds up one foot for inspection*) Look! I've lost one of my boots!

RANGER: I'm not surprised. It's a wonder to me you didn't jump clean out of your clothes when you saw your stepbrothers getting on their horses.

JIMINY: If I just had more time, I'd go back and look for it, but my stepbrothers will be here any minute. Golly, I can't bear to think of losing one of my beautiful boots. I'll never get another pair.

RANGER: Don't fret yourself, son. I'll go back a ways and take a look around. Maybe I'll find it.

JIMINY: Gee! Thanks, Mister. Thanks a lot.

RANGER (*Starts to leave, turns and hands* JIMINY *a golden whistle on a golden cord*): And say, Pardner, if you should ever need me in a hurry, just blow a good loud blast on this golden whistle, and I'll come a-hootin'!

JIMINY (*Slipping whistle cord around his neck*): If I ever get into trouble, you'll be the first feller I'll whistle for. (RANGER *exits.* JIMINY *whistles a tune as he finishes hiding his cowboy gear. He puts the hat, boot and holster under the bunk, the rest of the clothing under the blanket. As he hides the last article, his stepbrothers enter.* JIMINY *seizes the broom, and sweeps madly as they approach.*)

CHUCKY: That Jiminy Cinders had better have plenty of grub rustled up for us, if he knows what's good for him.

BUCKY (*Throwing himself into a chair*): Here, you little weasel, take off my boots! (JIMINY *kneels to help* BUCKY *with his boots.*)

LUCKY (*Flopping into another chair and throwing his hat on the floor*): And hang up my hat. (*Wiping face with bandanna*) Wow! It sure is hot and dusty!

CHUCKY (*Going to water bucket, lifts empty dipper*): What's this? No drinking water in the house! (*Grabs the kneeling* JIMINY *by the collar and pulls him to his feet*) You lazy, good-for-nothing! You forgot to go to the spring! (*Thrusting bucket into his hand and giving him a shove*) Now get us some water—pronto!

BUCKY (*Going to kettle at fireplace*): Wait a minute, Chucky. This little rat hasn't even started the stew! (*He grabs* JIMINY *by the other arm.*) What's the idea? What have you been doing all afternoon?

JIMINY (*Terrified*): I—I . . . well . . . it took a long time to sweep out the bunkhouse.

LUCKY (*Rising and joining group in a threatening manner*): Sweep out the bunkhouse, eh? (*Stooping and peering under the bunks*) From what I can see, there's just as much dust under them thar bunks as there was yesterday.

CHUCKY: Jiminy Cinders, what have you been up to?

JIMINY (*Half crying*): Nothing! Nothing!

LUCKY (*Pretending to unfasten his belt*): Maybe a good dose of strap-leather will loosen his tongue.

JIMINY: No! No! Please! Let me go! I'll make the stew. I'll get the water. It won't take me a minute. Please, please! I'll have your supper ready in a jiffy.

CHUCKY (*Releasing him with a shove*): Well, see that you do.

JIMINY: You just sit down and rest. Did you have a good time at the rodeo? Did you win any prizes?

CHUCKY: Don't talk to me about the rodeo! It was all a fake!

JIMINY: A fake?

BUCKY: Yes, a fake. Can't you understand English?

LUCKY: Some little kid nobody ever heard of won all the events.

CHUCKY: His name wasn't even listed among the riders.

JIMINY: How big was he? What did he look like?

CHUCKY: How should we know? We didn't even pay any attention to him!

BUCKY: When they start lettin' kids like that in a rodeo, I'm through!

LUCKY: The whole thing's a fake . . . when a shrimp like that can walk off with the golden spurs!

JIMINY: The golden spurs? Did he really win the golden spurs?

CHUCKY: Well, he would have won them, but he rode off

with some big tall ranger in a yellow outfit before they ever got round to handing out the prizes.

JIMINY (*Half to himself*): The golden spurs! I can't believe it! I just can't believe it.

LUCKY (*Slapping* JIMINY *on the shoulder*): Well, what are you doing, standing there daydreaming! Get moving with that grub you promised us.

JIMINY (*Quickly*): O.K., O.K.! (*Runs to fireplace*) I'll stir up the fire and then go for the water. (*Pretends to stir up fire and add wood.*)

CHUCKY: I still can't get over it. What kind of judges do they have that would give the golden spurs to a punky little kid no bigger than Jiminy Cinders?

LUCKY: I'd like to get my hands on that kid.

BUCKY: He wouldn't ride in any more rodeos when I got through with him. (*Loud knocking at the door, repeated several times*)

CHUCKY: What's the matter with you, Jiminy? Can't you hear there's someone at the door? (JIMINY *runs to door.* SHERIFF *and* TWO DEPUTIES *enter.* SHERIFF *is carrying a large paper bag.*)

SHERIFF: Howdy, folks.

ALL: Howdy, Sheriff.

CHUCKY: What brings you out to these parts, Sheriff?

SHERIFF: The boys here came with me lookin' for somebody, Chucky, and we had an idea he might be around here somewhere.

CHUCKY: If it's for that cattle rustlin' up at the Bar-X Ranch, we know nothin' about it.

SLIM: The Sheriff already knows about that cattle rustlin', Chucky.

BUCKY: If it's for that fracas over in Clinton City, we know nothin' about that either.

JIM: Sheriff already knows all about that fracas in Clinton City, Bucky.

LUCKY: And if it's about jumpin' the claim on the Susie Cue Gold Mine, we know nothin' about that either.

SHERIFF: Some other time, maybe, I'd like to talk to you about that gold mine, Lucky, but right now we're looking for the winner of the Golden Spur Contest.

ALL: The Golden Spur Contest?

SHERIFF: Yep. You see, the winner rode away before he collected his prize, and we're out looking for him. Thought maybe one of you boys might know where he is.

CHUCKY: Don't you know him?

SHERIFF: Nope. I didn't go to the Rodeo. I was over in Clinton City on business, but the boys tell me he was a little guy.

CHUCKY (*Exchanging meaningful glances with* BUCKY *and* LUCKY): Oh, he wasn't so terribly little, Sheriff. In fact, he was about *my* size.

SHERIFF (*In surprise*): Is that so?

BUCKY: As a matter of fact, Sheriff, he was closer to being *my* size.

LUCKY: It's a funny thing, Sheriff, but I look a sight smaller in the saddle than I do any other time.

SHERIFF: It doesn't seem likely it could be any of you boys.

CHUCKY: Why not, Sheriff? I had a mighty high score in the rope-throwin'.

LUCKY: And I know I beat all the others in the broncho-bustin'.

BUCKY: I made the fastest time in the ropin' and brandin'.

SHERIFF: Well, now, I wasn't rightly expecting it to be any of you boys. But we can easily prove it. (*Handing paper bag to* SLIM) Here Slim, see what you can do with this. (SLIM *opens paper bag and takes out boot.*)

CHUCKY, BUCKY and LUCKY (*Pointing*): What's this?

SHERIFF: The winner of the Golden Spurs left in such a hurry, he lost his boot. When we find the owner of this boot, we find the winner.

JIM: Would you boys like to try it on?

CHUCKY: Sure. Sure. I—I remember now! That's one of *my* boots . . . the special pair I always wear to rodeos.

SLIM: Then sit down and give it a try. (CHUCKY *struggles with boot which is far too little.*)

SHERIFF: Don't believe you're our man, Chucky. How about your brother here? (*Indicating* BUCKY)

BUCKY (*Examining boot carefully*): It *does* look a lot like one of my boots, Sheriff. 'Course, I can't be exactly sure.

JIM (*Pushing him into a chair*): Stick out your foot and let's try it.

SLIM (*Struggling to put boot on* BUCKY's *foot*): It's no use.

LUCKY: Let *me* try it. (*Struggle is repeated.*)

SHERIFF: You boys are just wastin' our time. (*To* SLIM *and* JIM) Come on, we'll try over at the Dude Ranch. Maybe it belongs to one of them city fellers.

JIMINY (*Tugging at* SHERIFF's *coat sleeve*): Please, please, Sheriff, could I try the boot?

ALL: What?

JIMINY: Could I please try on the *boot*? (*Sticking out foot*) See! My foot isn't very big.

BROTHERS (*Ad lib*): Certainly not! Who do you think you are? Of all the nerve! etc.

JIMINY: Please, Sheriff?

SHERIFF: We're in a hurry, Jiminy.

JIM: It wouldn't take long, Sheriff.

SLIM: The kid's feet are just about the right size, Sheriff.

SHERIFF: So they are! Well, sit down here, young feller, and stick out your foot. (SLIM *and* JIM *help* JIMINY *try on the boot.*)

ALL: It fits! It fits!

SHERIFF: Congratulations, young man. You are the winner of the Golden Spurs.

CHUCKY: But he can't be.

BUCKY: He wasn't even there.

LUCKY: He was sweepin' out the bunkhouse all afternoon.

BROTHERS: We can swear to it!

SHERIFF: I'm afraid your word wouldn't be worth much.

SLIM: Why not let the kid speak for himself, Sheriff?

JIM: Yeah, what's *your* story, Jiminy?

SHERIFF: Were you at the rodeo, Jiminy Cinders?

JIMINY (*Swallowing hard*): Yes, yes, I was, I was at the rodeo, Sheriff, and this *is* my boot. I lost it as I was riding through the brush on the way home.

CHUCKY: A likely story!

BUCKY: You little rat!

LUCKY: We'll fix you for this, Jiminy Cinders.

CHUCKY: It's ridiculous. The kid doesn't even own a pair of boots.

LUCKY: He doesn't even know how to ride. He's never been near a horse.

SHERIFF: Seems to me you have a lot of explaining to do, Jiminy.

JIMINY: I *was* at the rodeo! I did ride a horse—my very own horse! And I can prove it. (*Giving a loud blast on the whistle*) And I can show you the other boot—the mate to this one. (*Dives under bunk and comes up with other boot just as* GOLDEN RANGER *enters on a dead run.*)

RANGER: What's the matter, Pardner? Have these coyotes been bothering you?

JIMINY (*Running to* RANGER): I knew you'd come! (*To others, proudly*) This is my friend, the Golden Ranger. (*To* RANGER) Tell them I went to the rodeo with you!

RANGER: You sure did, Pardner! And a sweeter job of ropin' and ridin' I never saw.

SHERIFF (*Producing box from pocket*): Then it is my pleasure to present you, Jiminy Cinders, with the Golden Spurs. May you always wear them with honor!

CHUCKY: This is an outrage!

BUCKY: We won't stand for this.

LUCKY (*Grabbing box*): Anything that belongs to Jiminy Cinders belongs to us. We're his guardians.

RANGER (*Seizing box*): That's where you're wrong, Mister. *I* am Jiminy's guardian. From now on the boy's in my care.

ALL: *What?*

JIMINY: Is it really true?

RANGER: It's true all right. (*Handing papers to* SHERIFF) And here are the papers to prove it. Jiminy Cinders is my sister's boy. I've been searching for him for weeks . . . ever since I came back from the East. These papers prove that before she died, she placed him in my care.

CHUCKY: Then get out of here.

BUCKY: Good riddance to bad rubbish!

LUCKY: There's no room for you in our house.

RANGER: It isn't your house any longer. It belongs to Jiminy Cinders. The deed is there to prove it.

CHUCKY: But where are we to go?

SHERIFF: There won't be much trouble about that, boys. We were only waiting to settle this business of the Golden Spurs before we broke the news to you.

BROTHERS: What news?

SLIM: The cattle rustlin' at the Bar-X Ranch.

JIM: The fracas at Clinton City.

SHERIFF: And the claim at the Susie Cue Gold Mine! They've all caught up with you, boys. (*Snaps handcuffs on nearest brother, as* SLIM *and* JIM *handcuff the other two.*) So come along with us and see how you like your new home—the one with the barred windows and the big iron door! Take 'em away, men. (SLIM *and* JIM *exit with three brothers.*) Congratulations again, Jiminy, and thanks to you, Ranger, for your good work. This young fellow is a real cowboy, if I ever saw one! (*Exit* SHERIFF)

JIMINY: I can't believe that it's really happened to me.

RANGER: It's really happened, Pardner. You've won the Golden Spurs. Now all you have to do is make sure you keep that golden heart that belongs to every true cowboy.

JIMINY (*Twirling lariat in a burst of joy and shouting*):
I'm a cowboy born, I'm a cowboy bred,
And I'll be a cowboy till I'm dead! Yippeeeee!

(*Curtain*)

THE END

Robin Hood in Sherwood Forest

by J. G. Colson

Characters

EGBERT CRAFTO

PERCY PILCHER

DAVID O' THE COMMON

ROBIN HOOD

LITTLE JOHN

FRIAR TUCK

WILL SCARLETT

WILL STUKELEY

TOM THACKER

JACK PEDLAR

LITTLE HUBBERD

MUCH

OUTLAWS

ODLIN, *a soldier*

TIME: *Just after noon on a summer's day, in the time of* ROBIN HOOD.

SETTING: *A glade in Sherwood Forest.*

AT RISE: PERCY PILCHER *enters from upstage right, followed by* EGBERT CRAFTO. *Both are young men, very well dressed in the clothes of the period. They carry quarterstaves.*

EGBERT: No sign of Lincoln Green.

PERCY: Is this the right part of Sherwood?

EGBERT: Of course it is. Here's where we were sent and here's where we shall find the outlaws.

PERCY: Where we hope we shall find them. You haven't followed the wrong track, have you, Egbert?

EGBERT: Of course I haven't. Didn't we meet that silly oaf —David o' the Common as he called himself—coming this way? Wasn't he going to join Robin Hood?

PERCY: So he said. (*He moves down right.*)

EGBERT: And didn't he ask us if we had seen any of Robin Hood's followers?

PERCY (*Turning*): Ay, he said he'd heard they were here-about.

EGBERT: And didn't I tell him to cross the stream over there? (*He points left.*)

PERCY: I wonder if he tried it.

EGBERT: He would.

PERCY: And there's no ford. He'll get a ducking.

EGBERT: Hope so. We don't want him butting in.

PERCY: What a dunderhead. Belike he'll drown.

EGBERT: Serve him right! As if the outlaws would let a simpleton like him join them!

PERCY: But we're different.

EGBERT: Ay, we're different, Percy. Robin Hood will jump at the chance of having us.

PERCY: Then we'll go to the Grove of the Trysting Oak. Easy! Wonder where it is?

EGBERT: Somewhere in Sherwood, that's all we know. Those outlaws keep their secret well. Their lives depend on it. We'll never find out where it is till we're fully fledged merry men.

PERCY: And it's somewhere near this glade?

EGBERT: It is. Our information was good. This is the outlaw's path and one of them may come along at any minute. (*Noise of footsteps offstage right*)

PERCY: You think so?

EGBERT (*Having turned to face the sound of the footsteps*): I'm sure of it. Listen! (*Noise of someone approaching through the thickets.*)

PERCY: Right as usual, Egbert. Here's one of the men.

EGBERT: Ha! Make yourself tidy. (*They straighten their doublets and hose.* PERCY *moves up center to* EGBERT.)

PERCY: That's better. Now to join these famous outlaws. (*Enter from between the trees on right,* DAVID O' THE COMMON, *a sturdy, shabbily dressed middle-aged peasant, somewhat dishevelled, obviously in a hurry and a little perturbed.*)

DAVID: Hi! There you are, masters! Feared I shouldn't catch ye.

EGBERT: David o' the Common! Again!

PERCY: What do you want this time, you good-for-nothing yokel?

DAVID: That stream over there. The one you told I to ford. I be fair out of breath. (*He sinks down on the log down right.*) I ran after ye to tell ye not to cross.

EGBERT: Oh, did you!

DAVID: Ay. It be too deep.

PERCY: We know. But how did you find us? (*He moves above and left of small log.*)

DAVID: Followed your tracks, I did. You said you'd soon be going back over the river so I came like the wind to tell ye that there be no stones but they're treacherous.

EGBERT: I don't care what I said. (*He advances toward* DAVID.) What I want to know is what you're going to do now.

DAVID: Find Robin Hood. I've no home, nothing of my own. I be seeking a free life in the greenwood. Likely he won't have me, though.

PERCY: I'm sure he won't.

EGBERT: As a matter of fact, we're the sort of fellows he wants. We're going to join him.

DAVID: What, you masters! Life in Sherwood be hard. Be ye wise?

PERCY: Of course we are. We know our business.

EGBERT: But how a down-at-heel peasant like you dare be so presumptuous as to hope to enroll himself in that gallant band is beyond my understanding.

DAVID: And I don't understand either. Them fine words be too much for I.

EGBERT: Then understand this, David o' the Common, you're not going to sit on that log all day.

PERCY: You'd better be going.

DAVID: I'll bide my time a bit.

EGBERT: You won't. You'll go away from this glade at once. We're not going to have our plans upset by homeless vagabonds.

DAVID: Homeless, says ye. Have you a home then, master?

EGBERT: Of course I have, impudent knave.

DAVID: Then why be ye wanting to live with Robin in the forest?

EGBERT (*Advancing toward* DAVID, *raising his staff threateningly*): You get along or I'll put this staff about your ears.

DAVID (*Rising*): Easy, master, easy.

PERCY: Get along, fellow, and be quick about it, or . . . (*He too menaces* DAVID *with his quarterstaff, as* LITTLE JOHN, *wearing a friar's robe over his Lincoln green and carrying a staff, enters from upstage left center.*)

LITTLE JOHN: Hold, masters! (*He comes down center.*) If there's any quarterstaff play, let me join in.

PERCY: What, you, a friar? (LITTLE JOHN *waves his quarterstaff aggressively.*)

LITTLE JOHN: Ay, fellow, I know how to handle this. (*He indicates his staff.*) Come on, try your skill with me.

PERCY (*Backing away a little*): N-No!

LITTLE JOHN: I thought not. Two to one is about your mark. (EGBERT *and* PERCY *both back away to left, leaving* JOHN *center,* DAVID *down right,* PERCY *left center and* EGBERT *down left.*)

EGBERT: Steady, now, steady. (*From upstage right* FRIAR TUCK, *dressed in the traditional friar's garb of the period, enters, surveys the scene, then moves downstage between* LITTLE JOHN *and* DAVID.)

TUCK: What goes on here?

LITTLE JOHN (*Turning*): Ho there, Friar. Two fellows chastising him (*Points to* DAVID), so it's time for me to strike a blow or two.

TUCK (*To* EGBERT *and* PERCY): What has he done?

EGBERT: He's impudent.

TUCK (*Moving down to* DAVID *and gazing into his face*): No impudence there. Why do you ill-treat him?

EGBERT: He needs a lesson. We're sending him about his business. That rascally ragamuffin is hanging about here trying to join Robin Hood's band.

TUCK: So that's the sum of it.

LITTLE JOHN: You think, then, that only well-dressed men are admitted? Smart fellows like you, for instance?

PERCY: Ay, that's what we've come for. We're going to be outlaws merry.

LITTLE JOHN (*Moving left over to* PERCY): How do you know Robin will take you?

EGBERT: What, not take us? Have some sense, man.

TUCK: You'll have to satisfy him first. He has a special test which all newcomers must pass.

EGBERT: A test?

LITTLE JOHN: Ay, a test to find out what kind of fellow you are.

DAVID: Would he test me, too?

TUCK: Nobody is refused, my good man.

EGBERT: You know a lot about him. Perchance you know too much. Now could you two worthy friars be in league with Robin Hood? (*During the previous lines* ROBIN HOOD *and his men enter quietly from backstage center, and from between the bushes upstage left and right. Among his men are* WILL SCARLETT, WILL STUKELEY, LITTLE HUBBERD, MUCH, TOM THACKER *and* JACK PEDLAR. ROBIN *moves down behind the large log as he takes in the details of the scene.*)

ROBIN: In league with Robin Hood. Ha! Ha! And who's in league with Robin Hood?

LITTLE JOHN: These strangers think we are, Robin.

ROBIN: And think truly, eh, Friar Tuck?

TUCK: Ay.

PERCY: Friar Tuck! Shouldn't have thought it.

ROBIN: What news, Little John?

PERCY (*Astonished*): Little John!

LITTLE JOHN: Nothing of great import, Robin.

ROBIN: Then we'll hear it later.

LITTLE JOHN: As you wish. No need to wear these things any more. (*He takes off his friar's robe and hood, revealing himself dressed like* ROBIN's *followers, in Lincoln green.*) That's better!

ROBIN (*To* EGBERT *and* PERCY): And who are you?

EGBERT: I'm Egbert Crafto and he is my friend, Percy Pilcher. We were seeking you.

ROBIN: Seeking me? What for?

PERCY: We want to become members of your band, Robin Hood.

EGBERT: And we want to fight the Sheriff of Nottingham.

ROBIN: Ha! The Sheriff! So you want to help me plague him, do you! We'll see. But (*Pointing to* DAVID), is this other fellow with you?

DAVID: No, Master Robin Hood, I be not with them. I be David o' the Common.

ROBIN: And what are you doing in Sherwood, David o' the Common?

DAVID: I want to serve you, Robin Hood, if you'll have me. I be able to do odd jobs for you and your men. I be not clever but I can learn.

ROBIN: Of course you can. We all learn something every day.

DAVID: And perhaps, if I served ye faithful like, after a bit you'd let me wear the Lincoln green.

ROBIN: I might. But why?

DAVID: I be poor and everyone knows you help them that be in need.

ROBIN: But where do you live, David?

DAVID: Nowhere, master. I be homeless since our hut be burned down by the Sheriff's men on the common over the other side of Nottingham.

ROBIN: No relatives?

DAVID: No, I be on my own. Mother died soon after they set our hut afire. People laugh at me when I try to find work in the town. Say I be a country clown. Thus I be here in the greenwood.

ROBIN: So. (*He turns to his followers.*) Three more wish to live our merry life.

OUTLAWS: Ay.

ROBIN: Rich or poor, great or small, my followers must be keen woodsmen and men of real character.

OUTLAWS: Ay.

ROBIN: Is it your will that we put these three to the test?

OUTLAWS: Ay, Robin, it is.

ROBIN: Then rest yourselves. (*The outlaws squat on the ground leaving* ROBIN, DAVID, PERCY *and* EGBERT *standing.*) Egbert Crafto, Percy Pilcher and David o' the Common, if you desire to change your minds about joining us, you are free to go now. (*They do not move.*) Very well. Then you are prepared for our test?

EGBERT: We are.

ROBIN: And you, David?

DAVID: I be.

ROBIN: The test is simple. Each of you must walk for about three hundred yards into the forest, and then return to me. You must tell me anything and everything you notice.

PERCY: That's easy.

TUCK: Not so easy, my fine fellow.

PERCY: We came through the forest. We saw nothing but trees and bushes—bushes and trees.

EGBERT: But is that all, Robin Hood?

ROBIN: It is enough for me. Egbert go that way (*He points down left*), Percy Pilcher up there (*He points up left*), and David o' the Common make your way between those trees (*He points backstage left center*). Now go. Observe what you will. (*They move toward their appointed exits.*)

PERCY: Bushes and trees—trees and bushes. (PERCY, EGBERT *and* DAVID *go out.* ROBIN *sits on the large log.*)

PEDLAR: Don't think that one'll notice anything.

ROBIN: Will Scarlett!

SCARLETT (*Standing up*): Ay, Robin.

ROBIN: Follow Crafto. Don't let him see you, then come back and report.

SCARLETT: Trust me, Robin. (*He goes out down left.*)

ROBIN: Tom Thacker, keep an eye on Pilcher.

THACKER (*Rising*): I know, Robin. (*He goes out left.*)

ROBIN: And Little Hubberd—

HUBBERD (*Standing up*): I'm here.

ROBIN: David o' the Common is your man.

HUBBERD: I'll stick to him like a leech.

MUCH: Ha! Ha! Ha!

HUBBERD: Laugh at me, Much, son of a miller and—(*He draws a huge black-handled knife.*) Black Bartholomew will make a little slit in your throat. (*He caresses his knife.*)

ROBIN: No knives! Put it away, Little Hubberd.

HUBBERD: Only scaring Much, Robin. Look how he has changed color. (*The outlaws laugh.*)

MUCH: I'll give you change color. (HUBBERD *sheathes his knife, laughs at* MUCH *and moves off upstage center, carefully, as if stalking a deer.*)

ROBIN: Now, Little John, what happened to you?

LITTLE JOHN: We moved among the soldiers as you told us, Robin. They didn't see through my disguise and they didn't even recognize the Friar.

ROBIN: Good. Where are they now?

LITTLE JOHN: Where you said they would be. Close at hand over there. (*He points left.*)

TUCK: They asked questions about the Grove of the Trysting Oak.

LITTLE JOHN: Wanted to know if we knew the way to it. (*The outlaws laugh.*)

TUCK: Said they would receive a huge reward when they found it.

LITTLE JOHN: Even offered us a hundred crowns.

TUCK: Golden crowns, Little John.

LITTLE JOHN: Ay, a hundred golden crowns if by chance we should discover it and tell them.

ROBIN: How many men?

LITTLE JOHN: About three-score.

TUCK: Well armed but poor woodsmen.

ROBIN: What are they doing?

LITTLE JOHN: That's what bothered me, Robin. They were doing nothing.

TUCK: They seemed to be waiting for something. Yes, definitely waiting.

ROBIN: They're not waiting for the Sheriff, that's certain. I know for certain he's still in Nottingham.

LITTLE JOHN: They've some plan up their sleeves.

ROBIN: Ay, some cunning trick planned by that sly rogue in Nottingham.

TUCK: I'm sure of it. One soldier told us that the Sheriff had offered them two hundred crowns each if they found the way to the Grove.

LITTLE JOHN: And another ten thousand crowns between them if they captured you, Robin, alive or dead. They aim to surprise us.

PEDLAR: He'll stop at nothing to get you, Robin.

MUCH: We've always beaten him. It be fun. They'll never find the way to our Grove.

ROBIN: Well done, Little John and Friar Tuck. All of us must keep careful watch. We are more than a match for the Sheriff's men. We know where they are but we don't know their scheme. Friar Tuck thinks aright, there is mischief afoot. (*A noise backstage left center, and* LITTLE HUBBERD *enters capless.*)

STUKELEY: Back already! (LITTLE HUBBERD *comes downstage to the left of* ROBIN.)

MUCH: Where be your cap, Little Hubberd? (LITTLE HUBBERD *feels for his cap.*)

HUBBERD: Ah! I thought I felt it go. Lost it on a briar I did. That's right, lost it on a briar.

STUKELEY: Why didn't you pull it off?

HUBBERD: Didn't know it had gone, but stuck on a briar it must be.

ROBIN: Little Hubberd, where's David o' the Common?

HUBBERD: Isn't he here? Thought he must have come back afore me.

ROBIN: Did you follow him?

HUBBERD: Ay, Robin, follow him I did, but I lost him.

MUCH: Lost him! Ha! Ha!

LITTLE JOHN: Lost David o' the Common as well as his cap.

MUCH: You be a fine tracker, Little Hubberd.

HUBBERD: As good as you, I be, Much. I'll go fetch my cap. (*He moves upstage left.*)

STUKELEY: Better find David, too.

HUBBERD: Isn't that what I'm going for?

MUCH: Don't ye lose your hose this time, Little Hubberd.

HUBBERD (*Drawing his knife*): You mind 'ee don't lose your head, Much the Miller's son. Black Barty be sharp.

ROBIN: Away, Little Hubberd.

HUBBERD: I'm going, Robin. (*He goes out between the bushes backstage.*)

TUCK: It's unlike Little Hubberd to lose his quarry.

LITTLE JOHN: Ay, he's a tolerably good woodsman, although he's queer in his ways.

TUCK: You don't seem anxious about it, Robin.

ROBIN: No, Friar, I expected it. I'm not at all surprised. (TOM THACKER *enters hurriedly from up left.*)

THACKER: Quick, Robin, I must tell you . . .

ROBIN (*Looking left*): Wait, Tom—Pilcher is close behind.

THACKER: But Robin, it can't wait. (PERCY PILCHER *enters*.)

ROBIN: Enough, Tom Thacker. (*To* PILCHER) Ah, so you've returned.

PERCY: Yes, I've returned.

ROBIN: You've done as I bid?

PERCY: I tried.

ROBIN: Then describe what you have seen. Go on.

THACKER (*Interrupting*): A word, Robin, it's urgent, you must listen—

ROBIN: Hist! Bide your time. (*Turns to* PERCY) Go on, Percy Pilcher.

PERCY: This is silly—I noticed a few bushes and lots of trees. That's about all.

ROBIN: Any tracks?

PERCY: Can't say there were.

ROBIN: Not even of a rabbit or a deer? Any footmarks in the grass?

PERCY: Oh—er—let me see. I believe I saw tracks of a deer.

ROBIN: Buck or doe?

PERCY: How do I know? What does it matter anyway?

ROBIN: My followers must be skilled in reading the signs left by animals and by men. Our safety depends on it. (EGBERT CRAFTO *enters from down left*.)

EGBERT: Well, here I am. Ha, Percy, you've arrived before me! What now, Robin Hood?

ROBIN: A moment! (*To* PERCY) I have finished with you, Pilcher, for the moment. Now, Egbert Crafto, what have you observed? (WILL SCARLETT *enters hastily from left*.)

SCARLETT: Robin—

ROBIN: Not now, Will.

SCARLETT: Robin, you must hear me.

ROBIN: All in good time. Rely on me. (LITTLE HUBBERD *enters from backstage center.*)

PEDLAR: Little Hubberd!

MUCH: And he hasn't left his hose behind him. What have 'ee lost this time, Little Hubberd?

HUBBERD: I haven't lost a thing, Master Much, and if it's trying to be clever you are, I'll—(*He feels for his knife.*) I'll—(*He feels again.*) I'll—Black Bartholomew! It's gone.

OUTLAWS: Ha! Ha! Ha! He's lost Black Barty!

HUBBERD: Must have slipped out when I fell over that stone.

PEDLAR: Fell over a stone! Ha! Ha!

HUBBERD: Ay, a big bit of rock. I swear it weren't there the first time I followed that path.

ROBIN: Silence, all of you! Now, Egbert Crafto.

EGBERT: I saw nothing important.

ROBIN: Not important to you, perhaps. Did you, for example, meet anyone?

EGBERT: No, of course I didn't.

SCARLETT (*Bursting forward*): It's a lie! He met a soldier.

THACKER: And Robin, ask that Percy Pilcher if he met the same soldier.

SCARLETT: We saw them both. You know I followed Crafto.

THACKER: And I was stalking Pilcher. We saw them talking to one of the Sheriff's soldiers in the bushes over there. (*Points left*)

EGBERT: Balderdash! Your men imagine things, Robin Hood.

PERCY: Rubbish! A silly lie.

SCARLETT: Say we lie, would you!

ROBIN HOOD: Gently, Will, gently.

EGBERT (*Blustering*): Now, Robin Hood, we've had enough of this fairy-tale. We came to join you. We have taken part in your test. Are we members or are we not?

ROBIN: All in good time, Egbert Crafto, all in good time. (DAVID O' THE COMMON *enters from backstage center.*)

ROBIN: Ha, welcome, David. We're ready to listen to you. Tell me everything.

DAVID: No deer be grazing this way since dawn, but last night—about twilight I reckon—a great buck nibbled in yonder hazel thicket. (*He points upstage.*)

STUKELEY: He's right, Robin.

ROBIN: How do you know it was a buck?

DAVID: The marks be plain to see. Leaves and twigs be broken high up by his antlers.

PEDLAR: A woodsman, i' faith a woodsman.

ROBIN: What happened after you left us?

DAVID: I was followed by an outlaw, but he were that clumsy, I stalked him.

OUTLAWS: Ha! Ha! Ha!

DAVID: Just to show him I didn't like his way of going on, I took this. (*He takes* LITTLE HUBBERD's *cap from his pocket and holds it up.*)

PEDLAR: Your cap, Little Hubberd.

STUKELEY: Caught on a briar! What a briar! (*Laughter from the outlaws*)

HUBBERD: Hi, give me it back! (DAVID *throws it to him.*)

ROBIN: Continue, David.

DAVID: Soon afterwards, the same fellow be behind me again. I let him come close and then heaved a rock in his path.

LITTLE JOHN: Ha! Ha! We can guess the rest.

DAVID: Fell over it he did, and I borrowed this. (*He takes out* LITTLE HUBBERD's *knife.*) Came in very useful later on. (*He crosses to* LITTLE HUBBERD.) Here you be. Pleased I was to borrow it. It be the best knife I ever handled.

HUBBERD (*Taking the knife*): Thankee, David o' the Common. Barty be the best blade in England. Glad I am that you like him.

DAVID: I'm sorry I played a trick on you. Just couldn't help it.

HUBBERD: No hard feelings, David o' the Common. Friends be I with any who be friends with Black Barty here. Shake. (*They shake hands.*)

ROBIN: David o' the Common, you're a good woodsman. You know the ways of the forest. I'm pleased to welcome you into our band.

OUTLAWS: Hurrah!

DAVID: Thankee, Robin. I'll try to serve ye well.

ROBIN: We celebrate with a feast beneath the Trysting Oak this very night.

PERCY: What about us?

ROBIN: Will Scarlett says he saw you talking to a soldier of the Sheriff of Nottingham.

THACKER: So did I.

ROBIN: What is your answer to that?

EGBERT: It is a trick. An excuse to turn us away.

ROBIN: No trick! No excuse, Crafto. Will Scarlett and Tom Thacker do not speak falsely. The Sheriff will stop at nothing to find our hiding place. You were seen talking to one of his men.

MUCH: They be spies.

OUTLAWS: Ay, spies! Hang them. (*Etc.*)

EGBERT (*Shouting*): You're wrong, I tell you. Where is this mysterious soldier? Show me him.

PERCY: Ay, fetch him.

EGBERT: Show us your famed Sherwood justice, or is that, too, as mythical as the soldier your men talk about? If you believe there was a soldier, then show him to us. Produce him, Robin Hood.

PERCY: Ay, produce the man.

ROBIN: You shall have justice, Egbert Crafto. Will Scarlett, where is this soldier?

SCARLETT: He's with the rest of the Sheriff's soldiers by now, Robin, I should think, waiting for these two villains to lead them to our lair.

ROBIN: Can you bring him hither?

SCARLETT: Not now, if at all.

PERCY (*Sneering*): Pah!

EGBERT: Of course he can't; there was no such man. (*The outlaws murmur.*)

ROBIN: Hist! I need good men and true.

PERCY: But you don't need us, because of the cock-and-bull story these two men have hatched up.

THACKER (*In a rage*): You say another word—

ROBIN: Stop, Tom Thacker. (THACKER *quiets down.*)

EGBERT: Where is the soldier, Robin Hood?

DAVID: Listen to me. I didn't tell ye all. I noticed tracks of soldiers earlier this morning, I did. At times I heard them blundering through the forest like wounded deer.

PERCY: Perhaps then you saw this mysterious soldier?

DAVID: I did.

EGBERT: What?

DAVID: I did.

EGBERT: You did, eh? Then where is he?

DAVID: Behind the third hawthorn bush over there. (*He points.*)

EGBERT: Couldn't be!

ROBIN (*Smiling*): Then fetch him, David o' the Common.

DAVID: Come help me, Little Hubberd. Bring Black Bartholomew.

HUBBERD (*Brandishing his knife*) : We be coming. (*They go off left center.*)

PERCY: He can't be as near as that. He'd run anyway when he saw them coming.

TUCK: You speak as if there were someone, Percy Pilcher.

EGBERT: Pay no heed, Percy, they're trying to catch you.

PERCY: But suppose—

EGBERT: Shut up! This is another of their tricks. (*There is a disturbance backstage and DAVID enters through the bushes leading ODLIN, bound and gagged. LITTLE HUBBERD brings up the rear to help along the soldier with his prominent gleaming knife.*)

DAVID: Here be soldier, Robin Hood. (*They bring ODLIN downstage. The outlaws cheer.*)

ROBIN: Well done, David. How did you manage it?

DAVID: Dropped on him unawares after those two (*Points to EGBERT and PERCY*) left him. Didn't like his antics so I gave him a tap to quieten him like. Bound him with his own bow-string, I did, then gagged him with my neckerchief. Dragged him along and hid him in yonder hawthorn bushes.

HUBBERD: Lying there he were, trussed up like an old cockerel.

DAVID: Little Hubberd cut the strings round his ankles and here he be.

ROBIN: You're a clever fellow, David. (ODLIN *glares and*

splutters a little.) Ungag him, Little Hubberd. (LITTLE HUBBERD *does so.*)

ODLIN: I knew no good would come o' this. I told you so, Master Crafto.

SCARLETT: Master Crafto! Ho! Ho! So he knows him. Now who's lying?

EGBERT: Shut your mouth, Odlin.

ODLIN: Too late to shut my mouth. Would that you'd never opened yours to land me in this mess. I said Robin Hood was too clever. We're caught. I told ye as well, Master Pilcher. Now we'll all three be strung up.

PERCY: Will you hold your noise!

ODLIN: No, I won't. I've been banged on the head and pushed around against my will. Didn't I say it weren't a good plan for you two wealthy young gentlemen to try to sneak into the outlaws' band? Didn't I now? You had plenty of gold; what did you want with the Sheriff's reward?

ROBIN: So!

MUCH: Traitors!

OUTLAWS: Hang them! String them on the highest oak! (EGBERT *and* PERCY *try to escape but the outlaws prevent them.*)

LITTLE JOHN: Oh, no you don't!

HUBBERD: Let Black Barty tickle their ribs. (*The outlaws hold them fast.*)

MUCH: String them up!

ROBIN: Stop. That is not the way. You, Crafto, and you, Pilcher, sought to deceive us. You would have joined our company in order to betray our innermost hiding place to our enemy. You both wanted to go to our stronghold and go you shall.

PERCY: But I don't want to go.

ODLIN: What about me? I want to go home.

ROBIN: You shall, Odlin. Free his wrists, Little Hubberd. (LITTLE HUBBERD *does so.*) I have no quarrel with you. You're but a dupe of the Sheriff and his cronies. Return to your comrades. Tell them we know where they are and can take them when we wish. They're not safe in Sherwood.

ODLIN: I will.

ROBIN: Then go! Lead them back to Nottingham, to the Sheriff, and tell him that those two spies of his— (*He points to the cringing* PERCY *and* EGBERT) will be my guests until a ransom of six thousand crowns is paid.

ODLIN: I will, and thank ye. (*He moves off left.*)

EGBERT: It's too much.

MUCH: It is, but that soldier said you both be wealthy young masters.

ROBIN: You will pay and may it be a lesson to you both. Guard them closely, my men. Blindfold them and bring them along. Come, David o' the Common, with us to the Grove of the Trysting Oak.

THE END

The First Cat on Mars

by James Macpherson Harper

Characters

1st Pilot	Cookie
2nd Pilot	Cal
Younger	Bigger
Doc	Skipper
Tom	

Scene 1

TIME: *The future.*

SETTING: *The control room of a Mars-bound rocket ship.*

BEFORE RISE: *The audience first hears background noises. Then the voices come through.*

YOUNGER: Cast off all lines.

1st PILOT: Thirty seconds till take-off.

SKIPPER: Hey! Watch out for that boom down there! (*Pause*) All ready? O.K., then, remove all gantries! (*Noise of chains and pulleys*)

SKIPPER: All stations report!

TOM: Station one secure!

CAL: Station two secure!

1st PILOT: Station five secure!

COOKIE: Station three secure!

YOUNGER: Station six secure!

2ND PILOT: Station eight secure!

BIGGER: Station four secure!

DOC: Medical Station secure!

TOM: Station seven secure!

SKIPPER: Close all hatches! (*Noises of clanking*) . . . All crew members strap yourselves in! . . . (*Pause*) . . . Timer, begin the count-down!

VOICE: Seven seconds . . . six seconds . . . five seconds . . . four seconds . . . three seconds . . . two seconds . . . one second . . . zero seconds . . . (*Noise of blast-off builds up and dies off. There is a pause. Then the curtain rises.*)

AT RISE: 1ST PILOT *is at control panel;* 2ND PILOT *explains controls to* YOUNGER, *behind* 1ST PILOT. TOM *and* COOKIE *read.*

2ND PILOT: So you can see that if any meteors get in our path, the alarm will go off while they are miles away. Then the automatic pilot will change our course to avoid a collision.

YOUNGER: But I thought that there was very little danger of hitting anything, way out here in space.

2ND PILOT: It only seems that way. Come over here! (He *leads* YOUNGER *to porthole.*) Now you can see many stars and planets that you can not see on Earth because of all the layers of clouds and dust. What you can't see from here are the millions of meteors and asteroids that are ahead of us. If we hit a swarm of meteors on this trip, we'll be dodging all over the place to avoid them.

YOUNGER: But, with an automatic pilot, what's the use of worrying?

2ND PILOT: Plenty of use—just one of those little chunks could rip a hole in our hull so big that we'd blow apart, because there is a lot of pressure in here and none out there. So, we still have to be on guard all the time, even though there hasn't been an accident for a long time. (*Enter* DOC, *with a cat.*) Hey, Doc, how's the kitten today?

DOC: Tinker is just fine, aren't you, Tinker? (DOC *settles on the floor and pets cat.*)

YOUNGER (*Pets cat, too*): Gee, to see all those cows and pigs and chickens and even a kitten on this ship, makes me wonder what goes on.

TOM: Well, you'll get used to hauling a lot of different things, after you've been riding the rocket awhile. The miners up on Mars are going to need all the things we take to them. (*Cow moos.*)

2ND PILOT: Yeah, and if any more colonists go up, they'll need lots more food.

YOUNGER: But why don't the cows give any milk? Or the chickens any eggs?

TOM: Well, in the first place, they're all very young, so you can't expect any eggs or milk. And then, they were all given injections before we left that would cause all the food they eat to be used up, so we have to carry less food for them. It's something like the medicine they take back on Earth for liver trouble, only we give the injections to slow them down, not to pep them up.

DOC: Boy, I wish we could bring them out of it for awhile. I could sure use a real fried egg for a change, instead of getting powdered eggs, powdered milk, powdered fruit, powdered cereals, and powdered vegetables, all the time.

TOM (*Rising*): Yeah, it's a wonder they haven't figured out some way they could give us powdered knives, forks, and spoons. (*He exits.*)

2ND PILOT: Or maybe even a dehydrated cook?

COOKIE: Aw, I do the best I can with all that powdered food.

2ND PILOT: Cookie, you cook like a rocket engineer— everything all burnt out!

COOKIE: Oh, yeah? Well, you pilot this thing like a short-order cook would—everything half-done and on top of each other!

2ND PILOT: Cheer up! It could be worse! (*He exits, as* CAL *enters and goes to calendar to cross off another day.*)

CAL: Just think, boys, only 204 more days till we can sink our teeth in a real Martian steak—ahhh! (*Enter* BIG-GER.)

BIGGER: Well, here's old Calendar Cal himself! I thought you'd be back there giving all our water supply to your precious posies!

CAL: Don't make fun of those seedlings, Bigger. They're going to make big changes in the farming up there.

YOUNGER: Gee whiz, can't they even raise their own seed-lings?

CAL: Well, with these new varieties, their crops will be larger, and they can feed more people. Then we'll take more colonists up, so they can mine more minerals and smelt more metals for us to carry back to earth. And without some of those tough metals in the hull of this baby (*He pats the hull.*), we wouldn't be as safe as we are. Why, six or seven years ago, a meteor the size of a pea could rip us wide open—now they hardly make a dent. (*Enter* SKIPPER)

BIGGER: Oh, sure, now it takes only one the size of a peanut to tear us apart. That's what I call real progress!

SKIPPER: Glad you men brought the subject up. We're approaching the danger zone now, so we'll have several Emergency Drills in the next few days. (*Crosses left*)

BIGGER: Aw, Skipper, there hasn't been a ship hit by a large meteor in three years.

SKIPPER: Well, Bigger, up till now, our detection screens have been working perfectly, and the Emergency Pilot is ready to throw us into a new course in a split-second, but if we should enter a swarm of meteors too dense for our computing machines to handle, or if our machinery should stop for a second, the Emergency Drills could mean life-or-death to all of us! Any questions?—Very well, then, get Tinker out of the way, and everyone to his Emergency Station! Doc, you get your first-aid equipment set up. The drill will begin in two minutes. (*All exit, except* BIGGER, *as* SKIPPER *turns to the microphone.* 1ST PILOT *is still at the controls.* BIGGER *turns to face the audience.*)

BIGGER: Join the Space-Force, boys. Fill up on de-e-e-licious, de-e-e-hydrated delicacies; see last year's movies; take 258-day, one-way trips to Mars . . . straight up; see all the stars and planets, up real close; make friends with all kinds of meteors; count 'em as they go past; see all the . . .

SKIPPER (*Turns*): Bigger!

BIGGER: Yes sir! (*Hurries off.*)

SKIPPER (*At microphone*): Now hear this! We will run a series of three simulated emergencies. From the second I announce the location of each supposed hit, your stations will be timed by control instruments, and you should have each torn compartment blocked-off and pressurized within two seconds. The hull crew should

have a temporary patch in place within fifteen seconds
of the time they leave the pressure chamber. Hull crew,
double-check your suits. The alarm bell will ring in
thirty seconds for the first drill!

CURTAIN

*   *   *

SCENE 2

TIME: *Five days later.*
SETTING: *Same as Scene 1.*
AT RISE: 1ST PILOT *is at the controls.* YOUNGER *and* DOC
*sit, cross-legged, on the floor, with Tinker between
them. They keep her occupied with a ball of twine,
teasing her. A cow moos twice, offstage.* CAL *enters, goes
to the calendar and crosses off the date.*

CAL: Get your Christmas shopping done early, boys . . .
only 199 more days till we set her down on beautiful,
barren Mars. (CAL *sits in chair, to read. Enter* BIGGER,
ambling to chair.)

BIGGER: Yeah, join the Space Force, boys! If you (*Points at*
CAL) have the mentality of a child of three, and are a
perfect physical specimen—having one perfect eye, one
perfect arm, and one perfectly healthy lung, Uncle
Pluto and Aunt Venus want you! So you can learn to
go through meteor drills in half the time it would take
a normal, three-headed person. If you have these qualifications, and have never finished kindergarten, you may
some day command your own rocket ship! (*He sits in
chair.*)

DOC: Why Bigger, with all those qualifications, why aren't
you commanding this bucket? (*Enter* COOKIE.)

CAL: Yeah, Bigger could run this ship all by himself, with only Tinker to take the orders and run through all the emergency drills for him.

COOKIE: I can see him training her to run the ship and telling her to "Wake me up at half-past 257 days, and I'll do the landing."

BIGGER: At least I could teach her to cook better than you do!

COOKIE: Oh, yeah? If I know you, you'd be cooking "cat steaks" for yourself, before you even got close to Mars!

BIGGER: Well, she's my cat, isn't she?

DOC: Hey Bigger, you're not going to sell Tinker when we get there, are you?

BIGGER: I'd like to know why I shouldn't!

DOC: Well, she's a heck of a quiet little mascot and full of fun. I'd like to see her go along with us on some more trips.

BIGGER: Oh, yeah? Well, some of the colonists up there would pay anything to own the very first housecat on Mars . . . and I aim to make them really pay for this one.

COOKIE: How about the regulations?

BIGGER: It's all legal! They say that each rocket crew may have a small mascot of some sort . . . but they don't say you can't take one up and come back without it! (*He rises.*) I figure that in the next few trips, with more kittens, I can make a nice pile of money! (*Moving to doorway*) Well boys, I have to check our oxygen supply, before the Skipper checks on me . . . stay happy! (*He exits.*)

CAL (*Calls after* BIGGER): If you knock over any more of my plants, while you're fooling around back there, I'll make you happy!

1ST PILOT (*Turning from panel*): I thought it was funny when he offered to buy a mascot for the ship. But I suppose you find one like him on every . . . (*Alarm interrupts him*) Emergency stations, quick! It's meteors! (*Men exit, with Tinker. Alarm rings in short bursts. 1ST PILOT works controls. Explosions. Lights flicker. Panel lights flash in a frenzy of color. Then everything is quiet. A moment later, SKIPPER enters, papers in hand, followed by 2ND PILOT. 2ND PILOT adjusts dials on panel as cow moos offstage.*)

SKIPPER (*To 1ST PILOT*): Everything O.K. here? (1ST PILOT *nods.*) Good. We came through in pretty good shape. (*To 2ND PILOT*) Get that station yet?

2ND PILOT (*Nodding*): Yes, sir. We're in contact with Luna Station. You can go ahead now, sir.

SKIPPER (*Into microphone*): Hello, Luna Station, hello, Luna Station. This is U.S. Space Force Freighter 74-D. At 1300 hours and thirty seven point five minutes, on the fifty-ninth day of our scheduled run, we encountered a large swarm of meteors. We were traveling in assigned orbit, at 25,000 meters per second. Most of the swarm was passed through in thirteen point five seconds. We suffered three small rips in the outer hull, one large tear in the port fin, and numerous dents. No casualties or injuries. Cargo uninjured and intact. We are back on orbit. End of report from U.S.R.F. 74-D. (SKIPPER *looks through his papers, as* BIGGER *enters, followed by* YOUNGER.)

YOUNGER: Boy, that was some swarm of meteors, wasn't it? (*They sit in chairs.*)

BIGGER: Wait'll you've been on this run awhile longer. (*Enter* CAL, *who picks up magazine and sits on floor.*) Why I remember one time when we were out of fuel, out of oxygen, and out of food, and we were still millions of miles away from Mars!

YOUNGER: Gee! What happened?

CAL: Don't let him catch you with that old chestnut, Kid. We were back on Earth, hadn't taken off yet, hadn't loaded any fuel, food or oxygen; how could we get to Mars?

BIGGER: Aw, you guys spoil everything! I had him believing all of it! (TOM *sticks his head in the doorway, worriedly.*)

TOM: Hey! Have any of you guys seen Tinker? (CAL *rises.*)

CAL: I thought you had put her in her harness.

TOM (*Stepping inside*): Cookie says she was looking sort of sick, so he took her into the galley. When he turned around later, she was gone! We both looked all over for her.

YOUNGER (*Rising*): If she's sick, we'd better find her . . . maybe she's dying, or hurt real bad!

BIGGER (*Rising*): If you guys have lost her, you're going to pay me every cent I'd have gotten for her!

TOM: Hold onto your teeth, Bigger! I don't think she stepped outside for a breath of fresh vacuum . . . she's around, some place!

CAL: Yeah, Bigger, maybe she put on one of our space suits and went for a walk around the block. (*Enter* COOKIE.)

COOKIE: Did you find her?

CAL: Take it easy, Cookie, we'll find her soon enough.

YOUNGER (*Grabbing* COOKIE's *arm*): Was she very sick? Do you think she's dying some place? Where did you last see her? What . . .

COOKIE (*Shaking his arm loose*): Hold off, Younger. Give me a chance to answer, will you? She looked pretty sick to me, so I took her into the galley to give her some bicarb of soda, but, when I turned around, she was gone! (SKIPPER *turns around*.)

SKIPPER: What's the trouble?

BIGGER: Tinker is sick, and these guys have lost her!

CAL: I thought you didn't like the cat, Bigger. Every time I've seen you near her, your eyes showed dollar signs, instead of pupils!

SKIPPER: Let's stop the squabbling! We'll divide the ship up amongst us and hunt for her. Cal, you take the crew's quarters; Tom can take the animal's compartment; Cookie will check his galley, again; Bigger will look through the cargo; I'll check on the engine room; Younger and Doc can bring whatever first-aid equipment we might need! Everyone take off, now, and really comb the ship! (*All exit, except* 2ND PILOT *who takes over controls. Shortly after,* DOC *and* YOUNGER *rush in, making several trips, with bottles, blankets, hot-water bottle, first-aid kits, etc., finally exiting, leaving everything in a pile.* SKIPPER *enters, and stands over the pile, perplexed.* CAL *enters*.)

SKIPPER: Any luck?

CAL: No, sir! (*Enter* COOKIE.)

COOKIE: I looked everywhere . . . not a trace of so much as a whisker!

CAL: Boy, it looks as if Doc expects a major operation. (*He picks up each bottle*.) Here's aspirin, mouth wash, castor oil, iodine, and even a bottle of cough syrup! Now what in heck is he going to use cough syrup for?

COOKIE: If he can't find anything else wrong with her, maybe he plans to give Tinker a cough! (*Enter* TOM.) Any luck, Tom?

TOM: Not a bit of it! I'm almost ready to believe in

ghosts! (*Enter* Doc *with sun lamp, followed by* Younger, *lugging a pair of crutches. All look at the crutches, which* Doc *doesn't know* Younger *brought along.*)

Skipper: Say, Doc, just what are the crutches for? (Doc *turns to look blankly at the crutches, then at* Younger.)

Doc: Younger, old man, I don't think we'll need them . . . for a kitten!

Cal: Yeah, Younger! Don't you think they're a bit too short for her? (Younger *starts to carry them off.*)

Skipper: Now that we've covered all the places where Tinker could be hiding, I guess we . . . wait a minute! Where's Bigger?

Cal: He was back in the cargo hold. She could hide in a thousand places, back there among all those seedlings of mine! I'd better go help him! (*As* Cal *starts for door,* Bigger *enters, carrying Tinker.* Doc *rushes to take the cat. Others crowd* Doc *as he carries Tinker to chair where he examines her, with his back to the audience.* Bigger *stands, sheepishly, back from the group. He cranes his neck, to catch glimpses of what goes on.*)

Cal: How is she, Doc?

Tom: What's wrong with her, Doc?

Younger: Is she going to get well?

Skipper: Hold on, and let Doc make his examination! (*They stand back, without a sound or move, while he makes his examination.* Doc *straightens up and turns to* Younger.)

Doc: Take it all back! (*He points to the equipment.*)

Younger: What for, Doc?

Doc: Never mind! Just put it all away, again!

Cookie: What do you mean? Is—is—she beyond all hope?

Doc: No! I guess she'll live awhile longer.

Cal (*Slowly*): You mean she's crippled?

Doc: I mean there's not a doggone thing wrong with her! (*All grin and relax.* Cookie *leans over to pet* Tinker.)

Tom: Boy, that's a relief! I thought sure she was a goner!

Cookie: She certainly looks better than she did awhile ago!

Cal: How did she look when you found her, Bigger? (*All turn to face* Bigger.)

Bigger: I guess your plants and seedlings did the trick, Cal. She chewed up about a dozen of them, back there!

Tom: I'll be doggoned! I've heard of dogs eating grass when they were sick, but never cats!

Cookie: Well, you can still make your big pile of money, when we get to Mars, Bigger . . . she's still alive!

Bigger (*Looking down at his shoes*): No, I . . . I don't think I'll sell her, after all.

Cal: Well, what happened to you? Did you eat some of my seedlings, too?

Bigger: No . . . I . . . not exactly! (*He faces the* Skipper.) Commander, I . . . after the meteors hit us, I forgot to check the oxygen valves, and they were loosened by the jolts we took! (*Others exclaim.*) I just now tightened everything, but the reserve supply of oxygen is . . . gone! There'll be enough to get us there, but that's all! Tinker here (*He picks up cat*) was chewing on the seedlings right next to the valves, when I found her, and then I noticed the red warning light was on, and . . . and . . . that's it!

Skipper: I don't have to tell you men how serious this could be. It's like a lot of other things in our lives . . . we must all do our own jobs, or we won't live to brag about it! Bigger, do you know the regulations state that such an offense as this may be punished by the death of the person who endangers the mission or lives of the crew?

BIGGER: Yes, sir! All I can say is—I'm sorry it happened! I guess I must have been too excited about the meteors hitting us . . . I'd never been on a ship that was hit, before! But, that's no excuse . . . I guess I deserve anything you say . . . !

CAL: Skipper, I know this is serious—but couldn't you change the punishment? After all, Bigger caught it before any great damage was done.

SKIPPER: As Bigger himself says, there is no excuse.

DOC: Excuse me for interfering, Skipper, but don't the regulations say—that is, couldn't you—

SKIPPER: If you're trying to say the regulations state that the punishment is up to me, that's perfectly correct.

CAL: I think we've all learned a big lesson from this, Skipper. (*Others agree.*)

SKIPPER: Maybe it was a good thing for us all to learn a lesson so cheaply from one man's forgetfulness. In this case, it was Bigger who "goofed off"—it could have been any one of us.

CAL: That's right. (*Others murmur agreement.*)

SKIPPER: However, Bigger did commit a serious offense. But in view of the unusual confusion caused by the meteors, Bigger will be demoted to the grade of Rookie and will lose half of this trip's pay. Do you feel this punishment is too harsh, Bigger?

BIGGER (*Happily*): No, sir! Thank you, sir! (*The men relax, and the* SKIPPER *exits.*) If it hadn't been for Tinker, I probably wouldn't have checked the valves until too late! (*He pets the cat, tenderly.*) You know, I guess I never realized how wonderful a mascot really can be, until a few minutes ago!

Tom (*Goes over to pet Tinker*): Tinker, old gal, it looks as if you'll still be the first cat on Mars, all right, but I think those colonists up there will be darn lucky even to get a good long look at you . . . every three years!

THE END

Most Memorable Voyage

by Katherine Little Bakeless

Characters

CHRISTOPHER COLUMBUS
PHYSICIAN
INSPECTOR-GENERAL OF THE ARMAMENT
MARIO, *page-boy to Columbus*
CARLOS, *servant boy to physician*
FIRST ADVENTURER
SECOND ADVENTURER
RODRIGO ⎱
ALONZO ⎬ *ordinary seamen*
PEDRO ⎰
OTHER SEAMEN
OFFSTAGE VOICES:
  MARTIN PINZON, *Captain of the Pinta*
  VINCENTE, *Captain of the Nina*
  RODRIGO DE TRIANA, *a seaman of the Pinta*

SCENE 1

TIME: *September, 1492.*
SETTING: *A section of a ship's deck.*
AT RISE: PEDRO, ALONZO, RODRIGO *are leaning on the deck railing, gazing down at the water. All is silent. Then, as*

*one or two seamen slowly amble across the stage and
exit on other side,* PEDRO *and* ALONZO *turn to look at
them, and then return to their contemplation of the sea.
Presently, the page-boy,* MARIO, *enters left, carrying his
writing equipment. He does not notice the sailors. He
crosses to the sea-chest, downstage right, on which he
places his portfolio and inkwell. Moving back to a coil
of rope, he tries to shove it over toward the chest. He
looks around inquiringly, scratches his head, then notices the buckets. He gets one, takes it to the chest and
prepares to use it for a seat. He sits down, using the
chest as a writing-table, opens his portfolio, prepares his
writing materials.* RODRIGO *turns around, sees the boy,
smiles, and nudges his companions. They turn, and
watch the boy who is now bent over his laborious writing. After whispering to the others,* RODRIGO *leaves his
companions, saunters downstage and looks over the
page-boy's shoulder.*

RODRIGO: Well, well, well! As sure as I'm sailing over the
bounding main, it looks like real words! (*Laughing*)
Come and look, mates— (*Beckoning to his companions*)
real words. (PEDRO *and* ALONZO *laugh, but do not
move.*)

MARIO (*Startled at the first sound of* RODRIGO'S *voice, and
now on the defensive*): Hey, I didn't know you were
there. You startled me.

RODRIGO (*Laughing, but obviously liking the boy*): I did,
eh? Well, I sure didn't mean to. I didn't intend to
startle the Admiral's page-boy on a nice quiet sunny day
in the middle of the ocean.

MARIO (*Still suspicious*): Where were you? I didn't see
you.

RODRIGO (*Inclining his head*): Over there, leaning over the side—looking at the same stuff we've been looking at now for—what is it, Pedro? (*Looking back over his shoulder*)—over a week? (*Looks back at* MARIO) You know what that is? Dark blue-green salt water, that's what. And nothing else *but*!

PEDRO (*Sauntering downstage toward them*): Longer than that since we left home. Sa-ay. (*Bending over to look closely*) That does look like real words. Well, what do you know! Let's see if I can make out something. (*Runs his finger along on paper*) I can read figures. Yes, sir. (*Triumphantly*) There's a three.

ALONZO: Sure enough. That's a three, all right. And over there's a six. Well, mates, we're in fine company. (*Sailors are grinning. They like the boy, and indulge in a little gentle teasing.*) I never saw a page-boy who could read and write, did you, mates? What are you writing, boy? (MARIO *hesitates.*)

PEDRO: Come on, tell us.

MARIO (*Still on the defensive*): My master, the Admiral, wants me to learn. He says anything a person can learn is a good thing. If he *really* learns it, that is. He says knowledge—

RODRIGO (*Interrupting*): Maybe sometimes a person can know too much. (*All laugh heartily at this except the boy, who starts to answer, thinks better of it, shrugs his shoulders and sits down to his writing again.*)

ALONZO (*Insisting*): What are you writing? What's that three for?

MARIO (*Giving in, though he is really pleased to be able to show off a little*): I have written that we left home on the third of August (*Runs his finger along the page*)— that we sailed toward the Canary Islands; that when we got there we had to stay awhile because the *Pinta's* rudder had to be repaired.

PEDRO (*Slapping his thigh*): Why, that's right! The boy has it all down right. (*The three are much impressed and pleased.*)

ALONZO: Then what do you say?

MARIO (*Studying his paper and reading slowly*): Well, let me see. Oh! Then I have written that we left the Canary Islands on the sixth day of September, and the day after that we lost sight of land.

PEDRO (*Still chuckling*): Now, isn't that fine! The lad has it all down. (MARIO *smiles up at him.*)

ALONZO: Then what?

MARIO: Then I have written that as the days went by and we saw nothing but water, many of the men began to feel amazed at the great boldness of my master's undertaking. Some are still arguing about whether our world is flat or round. And still others have begun to cry and bewail, fearing that they may never return to their own land again. (*Pause. The sailors' smiles are gone. They are now serious.*)

ALONZO: Yes, go on.

MARIO: Well, the fifth day we saw the mast of some shipwreck floating by. Remember? (*They nod.*) Then a few nights later, there was that wonderful meteor that shot across the sky.

ALONZO: What else?

MARIO: That's about all. (*Pondering*) I was wondering what to write next.

RODRIGO (*Very serious*): I'll tell you what to write. Have you said anything about the wind?

MARIO: No.

RODRIGO (*Grim*): You'd better write down that the wind

has blown from the East now for nine days. It never changes.

MARIO: Why should I write that down? Is it important?

RODRIGO (*Making a grimace as he howls*): Aye! Is that important, he asks!

MARIO (*Insisting*): Well, is it?

ALONZO (*With forced patience*): Look, boy! If the wind always blows from the East, how are we ever going to get home? The wind is blowing us *away* from home. Just think that over and see if it's important. How could we sail home head into a strong wind? We'd never get there. (*The others nod and look grim.*)

MARIO (*Thinks it over for awhile, then looks upward and out right wing. Suddenly, his expression changes. Yelling and pointing*): Look! The wind isn't blowing at all! (*The three sailors follow his gaze, then they look upward, left and right, as if looking at all the sails. They run upstage to the ship's railing.*)

RODRIGO (*Excited, calling out*): We're becalmed!

ALONZO: The whole sea is like glass. (*Exit, the three sailors, running off left. MARIO stands spellbound, looking out over the sea in all directions. His gaze extends out over the audience as he turns slowly and completely around, taking in the whole horizon. COLUMBUS enters slowly from right. His hands are clasped behind him. He, too, is looking out over the sea in all directions but he shows no alarm.*)

MARIO: Oh, master! What are we going to do now?

COLUMBUS (*Smiling and at ease*): Why, we shall see how long it is before a breeze starts up again.

MARIO: But what if there is no breeze for months and months? We will just starve. Or die of thirst.

COLUMBUS (*Putting his hand on the boy's shoulder*): No,

no, lad. Don't worry yourself so. Just leave the worrying to me. And don't pay any attention to the alarms and complaints of these sailors.

MARIO (*Smiling up at his master, reassured at once*): All right.

COLUMBUS: You trust me, don't you, my young friend?

MARIO: Oh, yes. I trust you, my master.

COLUMBUS: That's right, my boy. Remember that if you believe you are right, then believe with all your might.

MARIO: Yes, sir.

COLUMBUS: Now, I *know* that the world is round. It has to be. Therefore, we are bound to find land if we just keep on going. (COLUMBUS *has taken his hand from boy's shoulder, and pounds one hand into the other to emphasize his last three words*) Do you believe that? (*Begins pacing slowly*)

MARIO: Yes, sir. Since you say so. (*Slight pause*) I was explaining that to Carlos.

COLUMBUS (*Amused*): Oh, you were, were you? (*Continues pacing, deep in thought*)

MARIO (*After watching his master for a few seconds*): Master, what shall I write now?

COLUMBUS (*His thoughts far away*): What's that? (*Looks up, walks over to boy, regards the writing materials*) Oh, yes. Well! Note down exactly when this calm occurred—the day and the hour. Then be sure to write down when the breeze starts up again, and from what quarter.

MARIO: Yes, I will. What else? (*Sits down, prepares to write*)

COLUMBUS (*Again pacing*): Have you written down the names of our pilots—the names of the captains of the *Pinta* and the *Nina*? Did you say that we have a physi-

cian and a surgeon with us? Also some adventurers,
some servants, and ninety sailors?

MARIO: No, I didn't know all that.

COLUMBUS (*During this speech,* CARLOS *enters left and
walks over to* MARIO): Yes, we are one hundred twenty
persons altogether on our three ships. Put that down.
Put everything down. Somebody may want to know—
sometime. (*Walks off left*)

CARLOS: What are you doing, Mario?

MARIO: I'm writing in my journal, can't you see that?

CARLOS (*Nonchalantly*): Oh, I see, I see, my learned young
friend. (*Throws himself down on the deck, leans against
the other sea-chest, and scans the sea. Suddenly, he sits
up, alert, shades his eyes with his hands, and stares out
over the middle of the audience.*) Hey, look, Mario!
There are some flying fish.

MARIO (*Looking at* CARLOS *and then out where he points*):
Yes, I see them. They're nothing new.

CARLOS (*Settling back*): I didn't say they were. I said they
were flying fish. (*Begins humming, while* MARIO *writes
laboriously for a while, grows drowsy; lays down his pen,
puts his head on his arms, and falls asleep. Slow curtain
with* CARLOS *still humming and dreamily looking out
over the sea.*)

CURTAIN

*   *   *

SCENE 2

TIME: *Later the same month.*

SETTING: *Same as Scene 1.*

AT RISE: *The three sailors are sprawled on the deck no
longer gay.*

RODRIGO (*Grumbling*): The end of another day and still this big ground swell pushes us around.

ALONZO: Anyway, I'd rather have this than that dead calm . . .

PEDRO (*Also grumbling*): As long as you're wishing, wish we'd turn around and go back. We've forgotten how long it's been since we saw land.

RODRIGO: The fellows on the other ships are worried, too. We ought to tie up the Admiral and run things ourselves and get home where we belong . . .

ALONZO (*Interrupting*): Sh-sh! Here comes the Admiral! (*They jump up.*) Let's go. (*Sailors exit quickly, right.* COLUMBUS *and* PHYSICIAN *enter, left.* PHYSICIAN'S *servant boy,* CARLOS, *follows them, but takes a position back by ship's railing during following speeches*).

PHYSICIAN (*As they enter, as if continuing a conversation*): —and they're getting into a state of nerves. They are all afraid, and fear is a terrible thing, sir. It may cause men to perform outrageous acts, you know.

COLUMBUS (*Chuckling*): They'd be worse yet if they knew I'd been keeping two reckonings.

PHYSICIAN (*Stops walking, shocked*): Two reckonings? How do you mean, sir?

COLUMBUS: Well, you don't think I'm telling these frightened simpletons how far we come each day, do you? The distance of each day's run I keep to myself. Only I know just how far we have come. What I tell the others is toned down a little. (*Laughs*)

PHYSICIAN (*Incredulous*): You mean, sir, that we have actually sailed farther than appears on the record?

COLUMBUS: We most certainly have.

PHYSICIAN (*Fussily*): But—but, oh dear! Do you think that is honest?

COLUMBUS (*Shortly*): No! I didn't say it was honest. These complaining, frightened, stupid fellows force me to do it. They are so foolish that they cannot even see that the most dangerous thing we could do now would be to turn around and go back. That's what they want me to do! Imagine it! (*With an impatient gesture*) Why, I have to protect them from their own ignorance. (*During the latter part of speech, the two adventurers quietly saunter on stage, entering left, and sit down on nearest chest.* COLUMBUS *has his back turned toward them and does not see them, while they sit there listening.*)

PHYSICIAN: Oh, I quite see your point, sir. (*Pause, still doubtful*) But it does seem as if we should have come to land before this. Today is the twenty-fifth of September —it is eighteen days now since we saw land—almost three weeks.

COLUMBUS (*Nodding his head*): Yes, yes. (*As if he's tired of hearing the same thing*) But it simply means that our wonderful world is much larger than we imagined it to be. (*His enthusiasm returns, he smiles and rubs his hands. His voice vibrates with profound conviction.*) However, we must soon be coming to the countries of Cathay! We might even land on the fabulous island of Cipango! (*His eyes sparkle.*) Oh, doctor, if I could only have known that great Venetian, Marco Polo. (*He places his hand on* PHYSICIAN's *shoulder and they start to walk the deck. Continuing, conversationally*) There was a man, doctor, who loved adventure—who had a powerfully curious mind. It is the curious mind that reaches out to learn . . . to find out things . . . Oh, I've dreamed of this western passage to India for eighteen long years (*Now having come to where* CARLOS *is leaning on the railing,* COLUMBUS *points at him*). Longer than you've been alive, boy! (*Laughs*) You see, doctor, it was Marco Polo's amazing descriptions which kindled the fire within me (*Pounds his own breast*) that cannot be quenched (*More and more excited*) until I see land in THAT direction. (*Faces toward right wing and points dramatically. Pause, during which the two AD-VENTURERS have business of whispering together; one shakes his head, the other shrugs his shoulders, then approaches* COLUMBUS.)

FIRST ADV. (*Smoothly, rather cajolingly*): Sir, your staunch belief after these endless days of seeing nothing but water, water, water everywhere, is somewhat, some-what . . .

SECOND ADV. (*Interrupting, impatiently*): What he means, sir, is that we think that it is plain recklessness to go on. We ask you to turn back.

COLUMBUS (*Regarding the man in amazed disgust*): You think I'm being reckless! (*Obviously trying to control his temper, he speaks in a low, very deliberate voice.*) You ask me to turn back! And what, pray, do you gentle-men know about navigating? (*Slight pause, growing more angry*) Why, you can't even read my maps. And why, pray, did you come along? I didn't ask you to. Did you come because you were interested in our quest? No. Not at all. You came because you thought there might be a chance of looting a rich city, and in that case you'd be the first to fill up your bags with gold and jewels . . . (*Looks around; addresses* CARLOS) Boy, go find Mario and tell him to bring my maps. Quickly, please. (CARLOS *exits left, running,* COLUMBUS *resumes his pac-ing, and says as if to himself*) I want to look at them be-fore it gets dark. (*During latter part of* COLUMBUS's *long speech, the stage lighting becomes dimmer, gradually.*

As light dims, red and yellow lights gradually come on in right wing, off. Business of ADVENTURERS *who whisper together with gestures, and exit left, walking stiffly.* PHYSICIAN *scratches his head, looks as if it is all too much for him, steps back to railing and stands there, looking out over the sea. Red and yellow glow becomes stronger.*)

PHYSICIAN (*Gazing out, right*): What a gorgeous sunset! (RODRIGO *and* CARLOS *enter, right, talking and gesticulating.* RODRIGO *is plainly urging* CARLOS, *who shakes his head in refusal.* MARIO *now enters, running in from right*)

MARIO: Here, master. Here are your maps. (*Hands a rolled bundle to* COLUMBUS. *He has also brought his own writing materials, and goes over to one of the chests and prepares to write.*)

COLUMBUS (*Beckoning*): Here, Physician. Before it is dark, let me show you on the map where I think we are. (PHYSICIAN *crosses over to* COLUMBUS. *Business of talking together and bending over the map.* RODRIGO *leaves the railing, and moves over to* MARIO. CARLOS *remains at railing, looking at water and sunset.*)

RODRIGO (*To page*): Now, tell me what you've written since you read to me before.

MARIO (*Leafing over the pages*): It's too dark to see.

RODRIGO (*Continuing*): I don't see what you could find to say. (*Laughs nervously*) We don't see anything but water. Sometimes . . .

MARIO (*Interrupting*): Well, I put down about the fireball that we saw that fell into the sea while we were becalmed that first time. Then about all the shooting stars we see at night. Then—the day we saw all those birds flying south, remember? (*Looks up at* RODRIGO)

And when we saw those birds, my master changed our course to follow them, because they were sure to be flying towards land.

RODRIGO (*Nodding his head*): Yes, sure. I remember.

MARIO: Then, after that, we saw thousands of floating sea-weed and plants, and (*Tauntingly*) then you all calmed down for a change, because you thought maybe my master was right, after all. (*Laughs*)

RODRIGO (*Uncomfortable*): Well. We can't keep on going forever. Believe me, when I get home from this trip I'm going to stay on land for the rest of my life.

MARIO (*Laughing*): Ho! I know you. After you get home and talk, talk, talk, about this, you'll change your mind. You'll be a hero. Then before long you'll be itching to get on a boat again . . . off again, on again . . .

RODRIGO (*Provoked*): Hush your babble, boy. I guess I've been on the sea longer than what you have. (*Looks around to make sure that* COLUMBUS *is not observing them*).

MARIO (*Unruffled. At the beginning, he was afraid of being teased by the sailors, but now he has grown bold with them, and he does the teasing*): Maybe you have. But that doesn't keep you from being scared now, like all the others.

RODRIGO (*Angry and scared*): Be still you! You don't know what things will happen before we get home.

MARIO: I didn't say I did, did I? But I think my master knows ten thousand times more than all you men who can't even read his maps . . .

RODRIGO (*Sullen, nudges boy's arm*): What else did you write?

MARIO: I said I was glad I was on the *Santa Maria* because she is the only one of our ships that has decks. She is the biggest, too. (MARIO *closes his portfolio. It is too dark to read. Afterglow of sunset light from right wing. Left of stage is darker*)

RODRIGO: The *Pinta* is faster, though. (*Looks off—right*) She's always ahead of us. Captain Pinzon keeps ahead so he'll see land first and get the reward. We haven't a chance. And the *Nina* (*Looks off, left*)—always behind —she hasn't got a chance, either.

MARIO (*Laughing*): Oh ho! So that's what's biting you. You're thinking of the reward for the one who sees land first.

VOICE (CAPTAIN PINZON. *A shout from right wing, off*): Land! Land! L-a-n-d! (*All on stage run to railing, at right.* PEDRO, ALONZO, *the two* ADVENTURERS, *the* IN-SPECTOR GENERAL, *enter, hurrying, from left, cross stage to others. All faces are looking off into the sunset.*)

RODRIGO (*Terribly excited, pointing out right*): There's Captain Pinzon on the stern, looking this way.

SAME VOICE (*Shouting, but it sounds nearer*): Land! L-a-n-d!

COLUMBUS (*Calling*): What ho! Captain Pinzon.

VOICE (*Shouting exultantly*): Land ahead, Señor! I claim my reward.

COLUMBUS (*Suddenly points out over corner of audience*): There! To the southwest. Look! What do you see, physician?

PHYSICIAN (*Peering, awed*): There seems to be a dark ridge along the horizon. (*The others on stage speak ad lib: "There! See? I see it. A low ridge of land! How far away, do you think?"*)

COLUMBUS (*Elated*): It appears to be about twenty-five leagues away. (*Turns his head upward and clasps his hands as in prayer. Then drops on his knees, and in deeply reverent voice*): Gloria in Excelsis. (*Others on stage, watching him, echo, ad lib, softly: Gloria in Excelsis.*)

COLUMBUS (*Standing again, cups his hands at his mouth, calling out toward right*): Captain Pinzon!

PINZON'S VOICE (*Off right*): Aye, aye, sir.

COLUMBUS (*Calling*): Change course, sir. Southwest! (*Slow curtain, with all faces gazing out at same spot—a little to front of stage right.*)

CURTAIN

*   *   *

SCENE 3

TIME: *The next day.*

SETTING: *Same as Scene 2.*

AT RISE: COLUMBUS, INSPECTOR OF ARMAMENT, *and* MARIO *are on stage. They look off in same direction, their manner showing their disappointment. Right stage is darker than left. Throughout following scene, light gradually grows stronger.*

COLUMBUS (*Pointing with his small telescope*): We were mistaken last evening. That was a cloud formation at sunset that looked just like a ridge of land. (*A few groans and grumblings sound from off.*)

MARIO (*Kicks at the rope coil*): Oh, what a gyp!

INSPECTOR: Nevertheless, we are certainly nearing land.

COLUMBUS: Yes, I think so. (*Calling off, as in last scene*) What ho! *Pinta!*

VOICE OF PINZON (*After suitable pause*): Yes, sir.

COLUMBUS (*Calling*): Change course again, Captain. This time, straight west.

VOICE (*Calling*): I think we should continue southwest, sir.

COLUMBUS (*Calling*): I disagree. Proceed W-E-S-T.

VOICE (*After a pause, disappointed*): Aye, aye, sir. Proceeding west.

PEDRO (*Enters left, running*): I think I see land, sir. (*He points. Others look, and shake their heads.*)

COLUMBUS: You'll all be imagining you see land, now.

MARIO (*Approaches* COLUMBUS, *whom he obviously adores, and takes his hand, smiling*): They all want to be the one who wins the reward, master.

CURTAIN

*   *   *

SCENE 4

TIME: *October, 1492.*

SETTING: *The same.*

AT RISE: *The two* ADVENTURERS *are talking together in low voices.* MARIO *is at left, writing in his book.*

RODRIGO (*Enters right, crosses over to downstage left, and peers off over audience, sweeping his gaze to right*): Mario, look here.

MARIO (*Lays down pen, approaches* RODRIGO): See anything?

RODRIGO: Doesn't that look like land to you?

MARIO: No, I don't think so. (*The two* ADVENTURERS *have noticed them, join them and also peer in same direction.*)

FIRST ADV.: I think that is land.

MARIO: Well, if you think so, why don't you tell my master?

FIRST ADV.: Because if it isn't, I forfeit my right to the reward later, even if I should be the one to see land first!
No, thank you.

SECOND ADV. (*Sneering*): That's the new law!

MARIO (*Bristling*): Well, the way everybody began to yell
out that they were seeing land, what did you think
would happen! My master had to think up some way to
make people more careful.

RODRIGO: Sure, sure. (*Pause*) I know who'll see land first,
but I doubt if he'll get the reward. (ADVENTURERS *grin
and nod their heads.*)

MARIO: Who, Rodrigo?

RODRIGO: Whoever happens to be on watch on the *Pinta*.
That's who.

SECOND ADV.: That's right.

FIRST ADV.: Stands to reason. *Pinta* is always ahead; her
lookout will see land first. (RODRIGO *urges* MARIO *across
to left where the page-boy has his writing materials.*)

RODRIGO: Tell me what you've been writing.

MARIO (*Consulting his notes*): Let's see. Oh yes—on October ninth the *Nina* was so sure she saw land that she
sent up her flag and fired her signal gun.

RODRIGO (*Ruefully*): Another mistake!

MARIO: Then—about the great flocks of birds that keep
flying southwest, and west . . .

RODRIGO: They must be going *some* place!

MARIO: And then my master changed his course to follow
the birds.

RODRIGO: What else?

MARIO: But with all these favorable signs, the crews are
angry at my master. They want him to turn around;
they say he is obstinate, and only tempting fate . . .

COLUMBUS (*Enters right, briskly*): Seaman Rodrigo, get

everyone on deck here who is not on duty. I have something to say. (RODRIGO *exits left quickly. From now on to end of scene, stage lights gradually dim, and sunset lights, as before, gradually brighten off right wing.*)

FIRST ADV.: Are you really going to turn round at last, sir!

COLUMBUS (*Turning on him aghast*): Turn around? When we are almost to our goal?

ALONZO AND PEDRO (*Rushing in, left, interrupt*): Look, sir, what we have just found! (*Holds out hand full of dripping seaweed. The two* ADVENTURERS *withdraw to railing, at rear.*)

CARLOS (*Entering, carrying a small wet branch of a tree*): Look, sir, what I just fished out of the water!

INSPECTOR-GENERAL (*Enters, carrying a small carved stick*): Sir, examine this, please. (*Hands it to* COLUMBUS) You will see that it has been carved. (*Others on stage show their curiosity and interest.*)

COLUMBUS: Yes, that has been carved by human hands. Now what more proof do you all need that we are approaching inhabited land? (*Other people have been entering*) You people have had no faith. (*Looks around*) Is everybody here? (*The entire cast and two or three other sailors, now on stage, looking hopeful and excited. During next speech the sunset lights come up*)

COLUMBUS (*Addressing all in a voice that vibrates with emotion. It is the most thrilling moment of his life so far*): From now on, a vigilant lookout must be maintained on each of our ships. I think it very likely that we shall make land this very night. I shall take my station on top of the fore cabin, but other eyes may be sharper than mine. (*Pointing toward left*) The moon will be coming up later. She is just past the full, and as it is a clear night, her bright light, fortunately for us, will shine (*Turns to face right front of stage, and points toward his goal*) on what lies ahead of us, and help us to see (*Reverently*)—what we shall see. Now let us sing our vesper hymn. (*He kneels, and all others drop to their knees as curtain falls.*)

CURTAIN

*   *   *

SCENE 5

TIME: *October 11, 1492—night.*

SETTING: *Same as Scene 4.*

AT RISE: *Blue moonlight overhead. All cast except CO-LUMBUS and RODRIGO enter and exit, cross downstage right, peer out, move on. MARIO enters and looks out over heads of audience from downstage center. ALONZO comes up to him.*

ALONZO: See anything?

MARIO: Not yet. Isn't it terribly exciting?

ALONZO (*Awed*): I wonder what kind of country we'll find?

MARIO: Maybe it will be a fine city.

ALONZO: I don't think we'd happen to come to a city first off. I think it will be a wild country.

MARIO: Where's Rodrigo?

ALONZO: He's up on watch tonight. We may land among savages and have to fight first thing. (*They move on, talking, as the two ADVENTURERS now come downstage and peer into the west.*)

FIRST ADV.: It's a perfect night.

SECOND ADV.: I really think he's done it now, don't you, Enrico?

FIRST ADV.: You mean Christopher Columbus?

SECOND ADV.: Yes. Don't you think we are approaching land?

FIRST ADV. (*Taking a deep breath*): Yes—I think I can smell it. (*They turn and wander on, as* PHYSICIAN *enters from left, crosses downstage right and gazes out for a few seconds. Turns and looks over the people on the stage.*)

PHYSICIAN: Mario! Look here, please.

MARIO (*Comes to him*): Yes, sir?

PHYSICIAN: Do you know what time it is?

MARIO: No, but I will go ask my master. (*Exit, running out right.* PHYSICIAN *continues to peer while* INSPECTOR-GENERAL, *entering left, crosses over to join him*)

INSPECTOR-GENERAL (*Tensely*): Anything new in the last hour?

PHYSICIAN: No, not in the last hour, but they say the Admiral saw some kind of light ahead, earlier in the evening.

INSPECTOR: Yes, I tried to see it, but I could see no light. It was around ten o'clock. Two others thought it might be a light on land . . . (MARIO *enters, running, approaches* PHYSICIAN *downstage*)

PHYSICIAN: Well, boy?

MARIO: My master says it is about two o'clock.

VOICE (*Of* RODRIGO DE TRIANA, *offstage, right, as yelling shrilly, from other ship,* Pinta): LAND! L-a-n-d! (*All on stage rush to right, downstage, and stare, mouths open.*)

MARIO (*Gasping*): Oh, I see it, I see it! (*Begins jumping up and down in his excitement. Glad smiles on all the intense faces.* MARIO *pulls on* PHYSICIAN'S *arm, screaming*) Don't you see it, Doctor? (*Points*) Look there!

VOICE (*Of* VINCENTE, *from the Nina, a muffled yell from*

offstage, left): What ho! Land! Land! (*Everybody is talking excitedly.*)

PEDRO: The *Nina* sees it!

ALONZO (*Reverently*): Señor Columbus was right.

PHYSICIAN (*To* INSPECTOR): Just imagine, sir, how Columbus must feel at this moment! (*A loud bang from off right wing*)

INSPECTOR (*Grinning*): The *Pinta's* cannon announces her first sight of land!

COLUMBUS (*Entering right, his face aglow, walks downstage center. All crowd around him. The manner of the* ADVENTURERS *and* SAILORS *is now changed to one of adoration.* RODRIGO *runs in from rear right, falls on knees at* COLUMBUS's *feet.*)

RODRIGO: Forgive us, sir, for not believing you!

PEDRO AND ALONZO (*Bowing and scraping ad lib*): Oh, thank you for not turning around when we wanted you to . . . Thank you, sir, for bringing us safely to land . . .

COLUMBUS (*With reverent emotion*): Go thank your God. Not me. (*Turns to* PHYSICIAN *and* INSPECTOR) Well, gentlemen, we've come to India! We will drop anchor now, and wait for daylight. We'll land at dawn . . . (*Quick curtain.*)

THE END

Top of the Bill

by J. G. Colson

Characters

PITTER ⎫
PATTER ⎭ *clowns*
MR. MASHETTE, *the ringmaster*
BOBBY
FRANK

TIME: *An afternoon performance of Mashette's Mammoth Circus.*

SETTING: *A clearing near the Big Top.*

AT RISE: PITTER *and* PATTER *are heard concluding their act in the circus ring, offstage left.*

PITTER (*From offstage, in the traditional manner of clowns*): And what is better than eggs, Patter?

PATTER (*Offstage*): What is better than eggs, Pitter? Eggs and bacon, of course. Silly old Pitter! Ha! Ha! Ha!

PITTER (*Offstage*): Off we go! Off we go!

PATTER (*Offstage*): Off we go, again! (*With the band blaring forth their exit chord, the clowns, PITTER and PATTER, come running and tumbling on the stage from the*

entrance left. The music stops. They wait for the ap-
plause.)

PATTER: How did it go? (*There is one solitary hand-clap,
a few "boos" and then silence.*)

PITTER: That's how it went! One old lady giving us a hand,
a few giving us the bird and the rest of 'em—

PATTER: Dead!

PITTER: Couldn't rouse 'em.

PATTER: No encore!

PITTER: Didn't expect one, did yer?

PATTER: Just hoped.

PITTER: There isn't any hope. They didn't like us. We're
finished. (*He moves down to a log down left and sits
on it in dejection.*)

PATTER (*Gloomily*): Rotten audience.

PITTER: It's not the audience. It's us.

PATTER: We used to make 'em laugh. What's happened?

PITTER: Dunno. We're just no good. We'll hear about it
when Mr. Mashette comes. Didn't you see his face in the
ring?

PATTER: No!

PITTER: Black as thunder!

PATTER: That's fixed it! I asked him to come along and
talk to us after the act.

PITTER: You did! What for?

PATTER: You know what for! Didn't we say it was about
time we had a raise in pay? I was going to ask him about
it.

PITTER (*Gloomily*): We're not worth a raise. No laughs!
One solitary hand-clap! And you're asking the boss for a
raise.

PATTER: It's not what you might call a favorable opportunity—but we can't alter it.

PITTER: You've been and gone and done it.

PATTER (*Looking off left*): Here he is.

PITTER: Now we're in for it. (MR. MASHETTE, *the ring-master, enters from the left. He looks scornfully at the clowns.*)

MASHETTE: Huh! (*He looks them up and down.*) Huh! Pitter and Patter, the comical clowns! Huh! Couldn't make a cat laugh!

PITTER: We're sorry, Mr. Mashette.

PATTER: We did our best.

MASHETTE: Sorry! Did your best! Huh! Worst show I've seen in this circus. Yes! Worst show I've ever seen and I've been ringmaster twenty years. What do you want to see me for?

PITTER (*Looking at* PATTER): Er—er—

MASHETTE: Go on, out with it. You've got plenty to say in the ring. Get on with it. I haven't any time to waste.

PITTER: Go on, Patter.

MASHETTE (*Sneering*): Go on, Patter! Never knew you to be tongue-tied before.

PATTER: Well, you see, Mr. Mashette, Pitter and I have been with your circus for fifteen years—

MASHETTE: I know! I know! What about it?

PATTER: And we're still getting the same wages as when we started.

MASHETTE: All you're worth! What's that to do with it?

PATTER: Well, we—er—thought you—you would—

MASHETTE: Out with it!

PATTER: We want you to consider giving us a raise.

MASHETTE: Give you a what?

PITTER: A raise in pay, Mr. Mashette.

MASHETTE: A raise in pay! Ha! Ha! What for, huh? What

for? (*They don't reply.*) You don't know. Nor do I. Not for being funny. Ha! Ha! A raise for not being funny! That's the funniest thing I've heard you say. Huh!

PATTER: We know we gave a bad show.

MASHETTE: Bad! That's not the word for it. It was terrible. Do you hear? Terrible! I pay you to be funny, don't I?

PATTER: Yes, Mr. Mashette.

MASHETTE: You aren't. Not one little bit. The audience came to laugh, didn't they? Didn't they?

PITTER: Yes, Mr. Mashette.

MASHETTE: And what did you pair of helpless, hopeless buffoons do? You made them weep. And you expect to be paid more for it. They won't come again. So I lose money, and you—you have the impudence to ask for more.

PITTER: We'll do better next time, Mr. Mashette.

MASHETTE: It'll be a bad thing for you if you don't. Mashette's Mammoth Circus doesn't carry dud acts. My public won't stand for it. Don't blame them either. You'll make 'em laugh next time or you're fired.

PATTER: Fired?

MASHETTE: Fired, I said.

PATTER: Oh, but Mr. Mashette, you can't do that. We've been here fifteen years.

MASHETTE: Times change. Audiences change. But you haven't changed, Patter. You're played out—the pair of you.

PATTER: Listen, Mr. Mashette, we've got some new gags.

MASHETTE: You'll need them.

PITTER: Give Patter a chance, Mr. Mashette.

MASHETTE: Hurry up then. Let's hear them.

PITTER (*Desperately*): Go on, Patter. Think of something.

PATTER: I'll come into the ring and say, "Mr. Mashette, do you know how to get into this circus for nothing?"

MASHETTE: Why should people get into a circus for nothing? Fat living we should make if they did. That's not funny.

PITTER: Let him finish, Mr. Mashette.

PATTER: I'll change it. I'll say, "Mr. Ringmaster, how could you get into somebody else's circus for nothing?"

MASHETTE: And I suppose you want me to say "How?"

PITTER: Yes, Mr. Mashette.

MASHETTE: How do you get into a circus for nothing, Patter?

PATTER: Walk in backwards.

MASHETTE: Walk in backwards! You're a fool, Patter. Why backwards?

PATTER: Because, Mr. Ringmaster, if you walk in backwards, people will think you are coming out.

PITTER: Ha! Ha! Ha! That's a good one! Ha! Ha!

MASHETTE: A good one! Huh! It's rubbish. Think up something better than that—or you'll go out—forward on your neck.

PATTER: Listen to this one, Mr. Mashette.

MASHETTE: I've heard enough. I won't listen to any more of your talk. You're played out. And you're on again soon. You'd better think up something funny. Pitter and Patter, the Comical Clowns! Huh! You're just nitter and natter. Make 'em laugh next time or get out. (*He moves towards the exit up left, then turns.*) You hear that! Make 'em laugh or get out! (*He storms back into the ring.*)

PITTER (*Moving gloomily towards Patter*): Make 'em laugh or get out. You heard him?

PATTER: Couldn't help it, could I? He's not trying to be funny, either.

PITTER: He means it all right. We're finished, Patter. We're too old.

PATTER: We're good for another twenty years yet.

PITTER: Not likely. (*He moves to the log.*) We'll be kicked out. (*He sits.*) We'll be on the road tomorrow. We just can't get the laughs any more.

PATTER (*Moving over and sitting beside him on the log*): Come on, Pitter, cheer up. We'll try again.

PITTER: Won't be any good.

PATTER: We're just a bit stale. Let's think of something fresh. Go on, Pitter, rattle your brain-box. (PITTER *scratches his head and is silent for a moment.*)

PITTER: Can't. Rattle yours.

PATTER: All right. Let's think. (*A pause.*)

PITTER: Thought of anything?

PATTER: I may have. Listen. Next time we go on I'll say, "Are you clever?" And you'll say, "Eat a feather." See?

PITTER: Don't like it.

PATTER: Try it.

PITTER: All right. (*They both stand up.*)

PATTER: Are you clever?

PITTER: Eat a feather. (*They look at each other.*) What next?

PATTER: I say "I'm not talking about eating." You say, "I am," then I carry on. Try. . . . I'm not talking about eating.

PITTER: I am. I could eat an elephant.

PATTER: I'd like a pancake.

PITTER: What do I say now?

PATTER: You say "Canpake!"

PITTER: Canpake! What next?

PATTER: I dunno.

PITTER: Neither do I.

PATTER: Think of something.

PITTER: Can't.

PATTER: I can't either.

PITTER: Fat lot of help that is.

PATTER: Afraid we're no good.

PITTER: I told you that.

PATTER: We're on in ten minutes.

PITTER: Don't I know it!

PATTER: Your turn to think of something.

PITTER: Me!

PATTER: Last chance. I've run dry of ideas.

PITTER: Riddles?

PATTER: They don't like 'em.

PITTER: String.

PATTER: String?

PITTER: Tricks with string.

PATTER: Don't know any.

PITTER: I know one. (*He takes a piece of string from his pocket.*) I come up to you and give you a piece of string, like this. (*He hands over the string.*) I say, "Here you are, Patter."

PATTER: What's this?

PITTER: Can't you see what it is, Patter?

PATTER: Looks like a bit of string.

PITTER: That's exactly what it is—a piece of string.

PATTER: Oh!

PITTER: Now Patter, I want to see how clever you are.

PATTER: Oh! I'm the cleverest clown in the circus.

PITTER: We'll see.

PATTER: What do you want me to do?

PITTER: I want you to do the easiest thing in the world. I want you to make that one piece of string into two.

PATTER: Easy. Cut it in half.

PITTER: Without cutting it.

PATTER: Oh! Got a match, Pitter?

PITTER: Without burning it!

PATTER: Without anything else?

PITTER: Without breaking it.

PATTER: Ha! I'd thought of that.

PITTER: And without unravelling it.

PATTER: You've fuddled my brain-box. Say all that again.

PITTER: Make that one piece of string into two without cutting it, burning it, breaking it, or unravelling the strands.

PATTER: It's not possible.

PITTER: It is.

PATTER: It isn't.

PITTER: I say it is.

PATTER: Let's see you do it then.

PITTER: Give me the string.

PATTER: Here you are! (*He hands the string to* PITTER.)

PITTER: Now you take the string like this—walk over to that log with it (*He moves to the log with* PATTER *in close attendance*), and place it on the side of the log in the shape of a figure two. See?

PATTER: No.

PITTER: I have now made one piece of string into two— the figure two, of course. Ha! Ha! Ha!

PATTER: That's not funny! Don't like it!

PITTER: Didn't think you would.

PATTER: Audience wouldn't see the string either—too small. Wouldn't get a laugh.

PITTER: Well, that's all I can think of.

PATTER: Bad luck, Pitter. Thought you'd got something that time—but you hadn't.

PITTER: Neither of us has anything.

PATTER: No.

PITTER: We'd better get out.

PATTER: Suppose we'd better. We'll only make fools of ourselves in the ring the next time.

PITTER: All right.

PATTER: It's the end of circus life for us, Pitter.

PITTER: Well, Patter, we've had our good times. We've made 'em laugh—

PATTER: And we've made them cry—but now, we'll just leave them, before they tell us they don't want us. (PITTER *throws his hat on the table and takes off his false nose.*)

PITTER (*Looking affectionately at his false nose*): Goodbye, old nose, we've had lots of fun together. (*He drops it on the table.* PATTER *takes off his false nose and puts that on the table. He takes off his clown's hat.*)

PATTER: Farewell, old hat. I've worn you for fifteen years, and now I won't wear you any more. (*He lays it down affectionately.*)

PITTER: Come on, Patter, let's get changed. (*Arm-in-arm they walk up the steps of the caravan.* PITTER *pushes open the door and goes in.* PATTER *turns on the top step for one last look around. He looks left towards the Big Top.*)

PATTER: One last look, Pitter. (PITTER *looks out of the doorway.*) It's circus done, old friend—a new life begun. (*He gazes sorrowfully off left.*) Goodbye, Big Top. Farewell, sawdust ring. We won't be with you again. We—we hate to go—but we've had our day—and tomorrow

there'll be fresh clowns and fresh acts for you. Be good
to them, won't you, just like you were to us.

PITTER: Come on inside, Patter, before you break down.
(*He pushes open the door, puts his arm round* PATTER,
*leads him gently into the caravan and closes the door.
At this moment* FRANK *rides in on a bicycle from down
right between the treewings. He dismounts as he enters
and wheels his bike to left center. He looks towards the
left.*)

FRANK: Rough going here, Bobby! Better get off!

BOBBY (*From off right*): O.K., Frank. I'll watch out.
(BOBBY *enters with his bicycle. He has one foot on the
pedal and glides over to* FRANK.) Don't know where we
are.

FRANK: Right in the middle of the circus.

BOBBY: Good! We'll have a look round.

FRANK: Didn't know there was a circus in this place, or I'd
have brought some money. Got any, Bobby?

BOBBY: Not a cent.

FRANK: Then we can't get in.

BOBBY: We can scout around, anyway.

FRANK: Good thing we rode this way. I like circuses.

BOBBY: So do I. Too bad we're broke. Shove your bike
over here and we'll investigate. (BOBBY *puts his bike
down near the bushes behind the table.*)

FRANK: This log'll do for me. (*He props his bike on the
log down left.* BOBBY *stands behind the table, inspecting
the articles on it.*)

BOBBY: Here, Frank! Look! (*He holds up a clown's hat.*)
A clown's hat. (*He puts it on.* FRANK *hurries to the
table, standing behind it on* BOBBY's *left.*)

FRANK: Gosh, what a collection!

BOBBY: Another hat! Try this, Frank.

FRANK: All right. (*He puts it on.*) How do I look?

BOBBY (*Laughing*): Crazy.

FRANK: What's this? (*He picks up a false nose and shows it to* BOBBY.)

BOBBY: H'm. Let's have a look. (*He takes the nose.*) I know—it's a false nose. The sort clowns wear. (FRANK *picks up the other false nose.*)

FRANK: Here's another. How do they go on?

BOBBY: Like this. (*He puts on the false nose he has taken from* FRANK.) Put it on.

FRANK: Suppose we get caught?

BOBBY (*Looking around*): Nobody about. Anyway, we'd soon pull 'em off.

FRANK: All right. (*They are now both wearing* PITTER'S *and* PATTER'S *hats and false noses.*)

BOBBY: You look kind of silly, Frank.

FRANK: Well, you don't look too handsome yourself.

BOBBY: This is fun, though.

FRANK: What's this? (*He picks up a stick of grease paint.*)

BOBBY: Grease paint.

FRANK (*Looking at it*): Number 20! White! What's that mean?

BOBBY: Not much. They all have numbers. We used them in the school play. Give it to me. I'll show you how to put it on. (FRANK *hands over the stick of white grease paint.* BOBBY *sits down on the bench, moves the small mirror to a convenient place and begins to apply the grease paint.*) Good thing there's a mirror here.

FRANK: I guess it's where the clowns make up.

BOBBY: Do their cooking here, too—by the look of all this stuff.

FRANK: What's in this old cigar box?

BOBBY (*Still making up*): Open it. (FRANK *opens the box.*)

FRANK: Sticks of grease paint. Lots of them.

BOBBY: Good. Put some on. There's another mirror there.

FRANK: Do you think we ought to?

BOBBY: No! (*He goes on vigorously applying the white.*) But it's fun! We'll dash behind that van if anybody comes.

FRANK: Hope they don't. (*He picks out a stick of grease paint.*) White!

BOBBY: Put that on first. Hand me a carmine.

FRANK (*Fishing in the box*): Carmine 3. There you are!

BOBBY (*Taking it*): Good. (BOBBY *puts on the carmine and* FRANK *begins with his white foundation.*)

FRANK: It's a bit hard.

BOBBY: It'll soften as you work it. Make a big mouth like this. (*He completes his mouth.*) And then put the carmine on your cheeks and eyebrows. (BOBBY *demonstrates.*)

FRANK: I've got you. (*He is still busy with the white.*) Can't get this white on properly.

BOBBY: Here, let me try. (*He applies the grease paint vigorously to* FRANK'S *face.*)

FRANK: Take it easy, Bobby.

BOBBY: In a hurry. My, you're beginning to look like a clown. Frank, The Frolicsome Fool. Put some of that carmine on. Use the mirror.

FRANK (*Getting busy*): All right.

BOBBY: Now I'll just finish myself off. (BOBBY *sits down behind his mirror again and* FRANK *is busy "doing" his mouth.*)

FRANK: Is this mouth big enough?

BOBBY: Let's have a look. Just the thing. Put some on your cheeks.

FRANK: I know.

BOBBY: Don't forget your eyebrows. Make them curl upwards like mine. (BOBBY *has finished. He gets up and walks downstage.* FRANK *is still busy with his cheeks and eyebrows.*)

BOBBY: How's that?

FRANK: Great! Wouldn't know you. Bobby, the Bashful Buffoon! (*At this moment, unseen by the boys,* PATTER *throws his clown's costume out of the window of the caravan.* PITTER *does the same, his falling on the steps.*)

BOBBY: Hurry up, Frank. I want to see the effect.

FRANK: There! That's finished.

BOBBY: What a scream! (*He does a cartwheel, landing near the costume thrown out by* PATTER.)

FRANK: Pity we can't get some costumes to finish the job off.

BOBBY: Wait a minute! What's this? (*He picks up a clown's costume.*) Gosh! Here is a costume! A clown's costume!

FRANK: Where did you get it?

BOBBY: Found it down there.

FRANK: That's funny. Didn't notice it before.

BOBBY: Neither did I. (*He moves nearer the van.*) Hi! Frank! Here's another on the steps of this old van. Look! (BOBBY *moves over to* FRANK, *who is behind the table.*)

FRANK: Just about your size by the look of it.

BOBBY: I'll try it. You take the other. (*He throws a costume to* FRANK *and begins to get into the other one.*)

FRANK: Suppose someone comes?

BOBBY: We'll hide. Put it on.

FRANK: Do you think we ought to?

BOBBY: Oh, it's fun. (*They are both getting into the clowns' "one-piece" costumes.*)

FRANK: How's this thing go?

BOBBY: It's a "one-piece" affair. Does up down the front. (FRANK *has a little trouble with the costume.*) Put your legs in first, chump.

FRANK (*Thrusting in his legs*): Bit tight.

BOBBY: That's because it's over your trousers. Pull! (FRANK *pulls on the trouser part of the costume.* BOBBY *continues his dressing.*)

FRANK: Got it!

BOBBY: Arms next. Get hold of your jacket sleeves and pull them through.

FRANK: Simple enough. (*He puts his arms into the costume. Then looks at* BOBBY.)

BOBBY: That's the idea.

FRANK: Bobby, you look like the real thing!

BOBBY: You will too, in a minute. Fasten it up. (FRANK *fastens the front of the costume.*)

FRANK: Is that O.K.?

BOBBY: The very thing. (*There are sounds from the caravan.* PITTER's *voice is heard.*)

PITTER (*From the van*): Come on, Patter. Time we were off.

FRANK: Somebody's coming out of the van.

BOBBY: Quick! Hide!

FRANK: Where?

BOBBY: Over here. (BOBBY *goes behind the side of the van and* FRANK *hurries after him. The door of the caravan opens and* PITTER *and* PATTER *creep down the steps.*

They slink silently off down right, carrying their bags.
The boys come out warily and peer after them.) Couple
of queer old guys.

FRANK: Down and out by the look of them.

BOBBY: They're going out of the field.

FRANK: Good thing they didn't spot our bikes.

BOBBY: We'll shift them. (*Music blares out from the circus*
tent.)

FRANK: The band. That's a lively tune.

BOBBY: Just the stuff for cartwheels. (BOBBY *cartwheels*
to the music.)

FRANK: And backward and forward rolls. (*He does a few*
forward and backward rolls in time with the music. The
band stops playing.)

BOBBY: It's stopped.

FRANK: Somebody'll be coming, Bobby.

BOBBY: Better get our bikes out of the way.

FRANK: And take these clothes off.

BOBBY: Not right now. This is fun. I'm enjoying myself.
We'll shift the bikes, though.

FRANK: Hide them in the bushes over there.

BOBBY: Good idea. (*They pick up their bikes and begin to*
wheel them towards the bushes, when the band starts
again. MR. MASHETTE *enters right from the Big Top.*)

MASHETTE: Get a move on, Pitter and Patter! You're on!
(*He sees* BOBBY *and* FRANK *and of course thinks they*
are PITTER *and* PATTER.) What do you think you're doing with those bikes? Huh? (*The boys stand stupefied.*)
Your new act, I suppose. Better be a good one. H'm!
Might work. (*The band fades out.*) Don't keep them
waiting. Don't stand there gaping, you fools. Get on
those cycles and ride in. (*The band strikes up again.*)
There's your call. Do you hear! (FRANK *and* BOBBY *sud-*

denly realize what must be done and they do it. After a
quick look at each other, they turn their bikes, mount
and ride towards the entrance to the Big Top.) And
make this act funny, or it'll be your last. (*He gets be-*
tween them, with one hand behind each saddle and
gives them a flying push into the ring. He follows them.
There is a roar of laughter from the audience, followed
by another. The band fades out. PITTER *and* PATTER
sneak quietly in from down right, carrying their bags.)

PITTER: We can't do it.

PATTER: No!

PITTER: We've never let a show down yet.

PATTER: And we're not going to start now. We've got to
go on. If we get the bird, we get the bird.

PITTER: Hope we're in time.

PATTER: Come on. No more fretting about. On with the
old togs. (PITTER *looks around the stage for their*
clothes.)

PITTER: Can't see them anywhere. Reckon they've gone.

PATTER: Gone! Don't be silly, Pitter. Some of the stuff's on
the table. I'll get it. (*He goes to the table and searches*
among the articles there. PITTER *moves to him and*
helps.) Queer! We put our hats and noses down here.

PITTER: Somebody's been up to something!

PATTER: Clothes gone! Hats gone! Noses gone!

PITTER: Now what do we do?

PATTER: Find 'em.

PITTER: Haven't time. We're on in a minute. (*The band*
plays again.)

PATTER: We aren't.

PITTER: Why not?

PATTER: Listen. (*They both listen to the circus band.*)

PITTER: That's our number.

PATTER: Do you think I didn't notice that?

PITTER: But we aren't on.

PATTER: I know that, don't I? (*There is a burst of laughter from the tent.*)

PITTER: And they aren't laughing at us. (*Another burst of laughter.*)

PATTER: Better see what's happening. (*They move to the ring entrance, up left, and look offstage as another burst of laughter peals out.*)

PITTER: A new act!

PATTER: Clowns on bicycles!

PITTER: In our clothes!

PATTER: Needn't look for 'em now, anyway. (*More laughs.*)

PITTER: It's working! Look at the audience. They're in fits.

PATTER: It's good!

PITTER: Not so good for us. Wonder where old Mashette dug them up. (*More laughs.*)

PATTER: They're bringing the house down. Here, I can't stand this. (*He moves downstage and sits on the log. PITTER joins him.*)

PITTER: Now we've had it. Why didn't *we* think of fooling around on bikes?

PATTER: Dunno.

PITTER: What do we do now?

PATTER: Dunno.

PITTER: You don't know anything. What did we want to go and walk out for?

PATTER: Your idea, Pitter.

PITTER: Yours, Patter. (*They get up.*)

PATTER: Yours, you mean.

PITTER: Wasn't!

PATTER: Was!

PITTER: Don't you contradict me, Patter, or I'll—

PATTER: You'll what?

PITTER: Do that! (*He makes a lunge at* PATTER, *who performs a backward somersault.* PATTER *does a forward roll over him. They chase around the stage in a mock battle, somersaulting, etc. They finish on either side of the table.*)

PATTER: Now, it's my turn. (*He picks up the plates and throws them one by one at* PITTER.) Take that! And that! And that! (PITTER *catches each plate and throws it back at* PATTER *who catches it.*)

PITTER (*As he throws*): Coming back! And back! And back!

PATTER: Clever boy! Hold these! (*He throws two plates quickly.* PITTER *catches one and transfers it to his left hand. He catches the second but has no time to throw it back.*) And this! (*He throws the third plate, which hits* PITTER *in the chest.* PITTER *catches it before it falls. He now has his hands full.*) And this! (PATTER *picks up a bag of flour and throws it, hitting* PITTER *on the head. The bag bursts.* PITTER *drops the plates on the table and splutters.*)

PITTER: Oh! Ah! I can't see. (PATTER *is convulsed with laughter.*)

PATTER: You ought to see yourself! (*He picks up the saucepan from the table and claps it on* PITTER's *head.*) That's finished the job! Ha! Ha! You are a mess! Funniest object I've seen for years!

PITTER: Take it off! Take it off! (PITTER *pulls at the saucepan, without avail.*) Help me, Patter, you fool. (PATTER *sits down on the log, helpless with laughter at* PITTER's *appearance.*)

PATTER: What an act! Oh! What an act!

PITTER: Get it off!

PATTER: I'm coming. (*He gets up and moves to* PITT *and grasps the saucepan handle.*) One good tug and

PITTER: You're pulling my head off!

PATTER (*Pulling at the saucepan handle*): Another go tug and off comes the saucepan. (*He gets it off t time.*)

PITTER: Ow! That hurt! (*The music from the band swe to crescendo.*)

PATTER: Hi! Listen! That's the end of our act.

PITTER (*Rubbing his head*): I should think so too.

PATTER: Don't be a fat-head. I mean that's the end of t act for those clowns out there. (*He points to the rin,*)

PITTER: I've got you. The ones who've borrowed o clothes.

PATTER: And taken our place. Come on, let's get into t van. We can see from the window. May learn somethir

PITTER: And you can clean me up. (*They move towar the caravan.*)

PATTER: You need it.

PITTER: You did it.

PATTER: Forget about it, Pitter. I'll give you a hand. want to know where these new clowns came from. (*Th go up the steps and as they reach the door, a perfe storm of applause bursts from the tent. The clow listen in dismay.*)

PITTER: Whoever they are, they've made it!

PATTER: We'll hear what they say. Come on inside. Quic (PITTER *and* PATTER *scuttle into the caravan. The ban plays an exit chord, as* FRANK *and* BOBBY *come bouncin off, breathless, triumphant. The band stops. The aud ence applauds vociferously. Shouts of "Pitter," "Patter etc.* MASHETTE *follows them on stage.*)

MASHETTE: Come back! They're calling for you! Take another bow! (*The boys return to the ring followed by* MASHETTE. PATTER *puts his head out of the caravan window.*)

PATTER: That's done it. (*More applause and clapping.*)

PITTER (*From inside*): Get this flour off.

PATTER (*Gloomily*): All right! Now we are finished. (*He pulls his head in.* FRANK *and* BOBBY *come back to the stage.* MASHETTE *follows wheeling their bikes.*)

MASHETTE: Splendid! Didn't think you had it in you! Here, take these. (BOBBY *and* FRANK *take the bikes and put them near the bushes.*) Wonderful show! Excellent performance! (*The boys come downstage. He wrings them by the hand.*) Congratulations, Pitter! Congratulations, Patter! (PITTER *and* PATTER *look out of the window open-mouthed.*) You were wonderful. Had 'em in fits! Best bit of fooling on bikes I've seen. And you didn't say a word the whole time. Why didn't you do this kind of thing before? If only I'd known you could put over stuff like this, I'd have doubled your wages. That raise is yours! Trouble with you before was that you were too full of talk. You hadn't enough action. Give 'em slapstick. That's what they want from clowns. Slapstick in your first act tonight and bicycle stunts in your second. You've made a name for yourselves. Keep it up, my lads, keep it up! (*The band begins to play soft music and the ringmaster hurries back into the ring.*)

BOBBY: Gosh! That was fun!

FRANK: Yeah. But, Bobby, what do we do now?

BOBBY: Dunno. Can't believe that ringmaster thought we were the real thing.

FRANK: He did. No doubt about that. Better get out of

here before the real clowns come along. We'll be in a mess if we don't look out.

BOBBY: You said it. Get these things off. (*They hastily get out of the clown costumes and take off the hats and false noses, during the following dialogue. They put the clothes they discard on the table.*)

FRANK: What a time!

BOBBY: Best fun we've had! Take it easy with that costume. Don't want to do any damage. The ringmaster, old—what was his name?

FRANK: Mashette.

BOBBY: Ah—that's it, Mashette. Old Mashette won't be back for a bit. He's bound to be busy in the ring with the horses—I saw them getting ready.

FRANK: By then we'll be gone.

BOBBY (*Laughing*): He'll wonder where his marvellous clowns have gone.

FRANK: But what about the real clowns, Pitter and Patter, he called them? (PITTER *and* PATTER *indulge in comic business from the caravan window.*)

BOBBY: Pitter and Patter have a shock coming to them. They don't know it, but they're famous. (*They are both out of their costumes.*)

FRANK: What'll they do?

BOBBY: What puzzles me is where they went.

FRANK: And me. How do you get this make-up off?

BOBBY: Rub it off on a towel as I'm doing. There's some cotton wool there, too.

FRANK: Hope nobody minds. (*They both remove their make-up, using the mirrors.*)

BOBBY: Frank, I've got it!

FRANK: Got what?

BOBBY: You remember those two geezers we saw go off with their bags?

FRANK: 'Course I do.

BOBBY: Bet you they were Pitter and Patter—on strike or something.

FRANK: Wonder where they are now.

PATTER (*Coming down the steps of the caravan*): They're here!

BOBBY: Holy smoke! (*The boys drop the towels and make for their bicycles.*)

PATTER: Here! Wait a minute! Don't go! (PITTER *comes down and joins* PATTER.) We want a word with you. (*The boys turn and come towards the clowns.*)

FRANK: No good, Bobby, the game's up.

BOBBY: Looks like it. (*He turns to* PATTER.) We didn't exactly mean to take your place. We just had to.

FRANK: You see, we were fooling about with your costumes, when Mr. Mashette came along and made us go into the ring.

BOBBY: We're very sorry. Hope you don't mind too much.

PATTER: Mind! Of course we don't mind. We're glad you did.

PITTER: More than glad—we don't know how to thank you.

PATTER: You've done us a real good turn.

FRANK: Good turn?

PATTER: Yes, my lads, you've shown us what was wrong with our act.

PITTER: And nobody's any the wiser.

PATTER: You've given us ideas for a new turn—"Pitter and Patter, the Cycling Clowns."

PITTER: You see, we saw a bit of your act.

BOBBY: Did you like it?

PITTER: 'Course we liked it. It was a "hit."

BOBBY: We just made it up as we went along.

PATTER: Did you, now? Well, you're clever boys. Yo
nearly brought the house down.

PITTER: And perhaps you don't know it, but you've save
our bacon.

FRANK: How?

PATTER: Between ourselves, our act was no good. W
couldn't get a laugh. We were hopping off for good.

FRANK: But you came back.

PITTER: Couldn't let the show down.

PATTER: What did we see when we got back?

PITTER: Two schoolboys in our clothes, doing our job fo
us.

PATTER: And doing it better than we did.

PITTER: Best thing that could have happened.

FRANK: Let's not say anything about it.

BOBBY: Keep it quiet, Patter. Then we'll all keep out o
trouble.

PATTER: We'll keep it quiet. Don't worry about that. We'l
try your cycling stunt.

PITTER: I know where there are a couple of bikes.

PATTER: Good! We can think up a few extra tricks—mak
wheels come off—

PITTER: Let the bikes fall to pieces—all sorts of things.

PATTER: That'll do for our second turn.

PITTER: What about the first?

PATTER: Easy! We'll do a slapstick act. One with flour an
stuff. You looked a scream just now with that saucepa
on your head.

PITTER: Did I?

PATTER: You know you did. We'll repeat that.

PITTER: Plates and all?

PATTER: Plates and all, with a few other things thrown in.

PITTER: And thrown about. But remember, no talk.

PATTER: That's it. No more cross-talk.

PITTER: We'll get some practice after dinner.

PATTER: Now, Bobby, and you, Frank, we'll have our costumes. We'll put them in the van.

FRANK: Here you are, Patter. (*He hands them the costumes.*)

PATTER: Thanks, Frank. Take yours, Pitter. (PITTER *does so.*) We don't want any more youngsters coming along and doing us a good turn, do we, Bobby?

BOBBY: No. Might be a flop next time. (MR. MASHETTE *enters from the left.*)

MASHETTE: Ah! Here you are! Changed already. Going into the town before the next show, I guess.

PATTER: As a matter of fact, Mr. Mashette, we did think of taking a walk.

MASHETTE: Be back in good time, Patter. The crowd'll be on their toes tonight.

PITTER: We won't be late.

MASHETTE (*Noticing* BOBBY *and* FRANK): Who are these lads, Patter?

PATTER: Friends of ours, Bobby and Frank.

MASHETTE: How do you do! Any friends of Patter's are friends of mine.

BOBBY: Thank you, Mr. Mashette.

MASHETTE: Like the circus, do you?

FRANK: Oh, Mr. Mashette, we love it.

PATTER: These two lads did Pitter and me a valuable service not so long ago.

PITTER: Helped us no end.

MASHETTE: Oh, they did, did they? Pleased to hear it.

Well, if they helped you, they helped me. (*He turns to the boys.*) Come to my circus any time you like. Walk in and don't pay. Sit in the best seats. Bring your friends. Come and talk to the clowns. And if you want a job in the circus when you grow up—come and see me.

BOBBY: Oh, *thank* you, Mr. Mashette.

MASHETTE: Don't thank me. Thank the clowns at the Top of the Bill—Pitter and Patter.

PATTER: Top of the Bill! You don't mean it, Mr. Mashette?

MASHETTE: Of course I do. You're Top of the Bill now. Had to put you there after your performance this afternoon. (*Band plays offstage.*)

MASHETTE: End of the act. Must be off. See you later. (*He goes out into the ring.*)

BOBBY: Hurrah! Free seats!

PATTER: Top of the Bill! Whoopee!

PITTER (*Beginning to cartwheel*): Whoopee! (*They all four cartwheel and somersault madly around the stage, the band trumpets forth triumphantly from the Big Top, and the curtain slowly falls.*)

THE END

The Crying Clown

by Mary Ann Nicholson

Characters

CIRCUS CLOWN
CIRCUS COP
CIRCUS OWNER
BOY, *about 9 years old*

TIME: *The first day of the new circus season.*
SETTING: *Outside a circus tent.*
AT RISE: CLOWN *is adjusting his oversized shoes. The*
CIRCUS OWNER *enters.*

OWNER: Wait just a minute, Clown. I'd like to talk with you.

CLOWN: Yes, sir, Mister Circus Owner. What is it?

OWNER: Well, it's hard for me to say this, Clown, but this being the first day of the new circus season and all that . . .

CLOWN: Is it something to do with my act, sir?

OWNER: Frankly, yes, it is. I might just as well come right out and say it. I don't think your tumbling act is funny any more. You had better think up a new act or find another job to do around here.

CLOWN: Oh, Mr. Circus Owner, you can't mean that. Why, I've been doing that tumbling act since I was only as high as an elephant's knee. My father was a clown, too, and he taught that act to me. He was the best clown in the business.

OWNER: That's just it. Everybody has seen it year after year and they are tired of it. They expect something new and funny. Now I don't mean to sound cruel, but you're getting older and you don't tumble as well as you did when you were younger.

CLOWN (*Still unbelieving*): Maybe you don't think it's funny because you've seen it so often, but there are children being born every day who will grow up and come to the circus. When they first see my act, they'll laugh.

OWNER: I'm sorry, Clown, I can't wait that long. Think it over and I'll be back in a little while to hear what you have decided to do. So long, Clown.

CLOWN (*Looking very unhappy, goes over and sits on bench and cries. The* CIRCUS COP *enters, dragging his billy club sadly behind him. When he sees the* CLOWN *crying, he begins to sniff, then joins him on the bench and cries louder. The* CLOWN *suddenly notices him*): Why . . . why are you crying, Cop?

COP: I'm crying because I'm sad. When I saw you crying, I wanted to cry, too.

CLOWN: But I'm crying because I will lose my job of being a clown unless I can think up a new act today.

COP: You're more than welcome to my job as cop. I hate it.

CLOWN: Why do you hate being a Circus Cop? (*He is interested.*)

COP: I have to be mean and chase away all the children

who try to sneak into the circus without paying. I hate to be so mean; I wish I could be a clown instead.

CLOWN: Children should be allowed into the circus; that's what it's for.

COP: I know, but some of them can't afford to pay for the admission tickets, so they try to sneak in under the tent when my back is turned.

CLOWN: Why don't you just keep your back turned until they all get inside? You couldn't be mean if you didn't see them.

COP: That's what I did once, and the Circus Owner saw me and did he ever tell me off! Wow, never again! If he fired me, I would have to leave the circus and I'd rather die.

CLOWN: No wonder you're sad. What will you do now?

COP: I don't know, that's why I'm so unhappy.

CLOWN: Let's be unhappy together. (*At this remark, the* CLOWN *and the* COP *fall on each other's shoulders and weep loudly. They do not see a small* BOY *wiggling under the bottom edge of the tent. He is half way through when he sees what is going on above him. He is so amused that he forgets himself and snickers. The* COP *hears him and stops crying long enough to listen.*)

COP: What was that?

CLOWN (*Sniffing*): What was what?

COP: I thought I heard somebody laughing.

CLOWN: You must be hearing things, there's nobody in sight. (*He takes out a large hanky and blows his nose violently in it. Then he holds the hanky up and it has a huge hole in the middle of it.*) Oh, dear, wrong hanky; this one's had a blowout. (BOY *laughs hard at this.*)

COP (*Looks around and spies* BOY *and pulls him to his*

feet): Aha, I've caught you this time. Trying to sneak into the circus, were you? I've already chased you away once today. Can't you take the hint?

BOY: Honest, Mr. Cop, I didn't mean any harm. I only wanted to see a real live clown.

CLOWN (*Cheering up*): You did? Well, isn't that nice!

COP: Then take a good look at him and be on your way home, Boy. Do you want me to lose my job?

CLOWN: Wait, Cop, I have an idea. The boy wanted to see me and I may not be a clown after today; let me do my tumbling act for him here now.

COP: Well, I've got my duty to do, you know . . . but . . . as a matter of fact, Clown, I've been wanting to see your act myself. Go ahead and we'll judge how funny it is. (COP *and* BOY *sit on the bench while the* CLOWN *goes into his tumbling act. He tries to stand on his head, ride a bicycle with his feet over his head, do somersaults, etc., but he isn't very good. He is so old and stiff that every movement is awkward and painful. He tries to finish with a graceful flip and lands flat on the ground. The* COP *and* BOY *exchange sad glances.*)

CLOWN (*Discouraged*): I guess the Circus Owner was right, I just don't have the old stuff any more. My days as a clown are over.

COP: Maybe you're just tired today . . . it is kind of hot and . . .

BOY (*A little too brightly*): I'll bet you were terribly funny when you were younger . . . I mean . . . (*Flustered*)

CLOWN: That's all right, Boy. I know what you mean. I'm too old.

COP (*Helping* CLOWN *up from ground*): Gee, I'm going to miss you around here, old pal . . .

CLOWN: And I'm going to miss you, old buddy . . . (*They fall into each other's arms with great racking sobs. The* BOY *feels sorry for them at first, but can't help but be amused. They reach into the hip pocket of each other's pants and draw out hankies, then they blow, and help each other blow and get all tangled up in each other in their grief. The* BOY *has fallen off the bench in laughter as the* CIRCUS OWNER *enters.*)

OWNER: What is all the noise about? What's going on here?

BOY: It's the Clown and the Cop, they're crying . . . Hahahahahahaha!

OWNER (*Watches* CLOWN *and* COP *and becomes amused*): Well, I'll be! It's going to be very funny, very funny. (*He laughs and startles the* CLOWN *and* COP. *He rushes over to shake their hands as he wipes away tears of laughter from his own eyes.*) Yes, indeed, I don't know when I've seen a funnier act. You two will be the hit of the season. Great act, splendid.

CLOWN (*Bewildered*): What do you mean, sir?

OWNER: Oh, come now, Clown. You don't have to play innocent with me. I saw you and the Cop rehearsing your new clown act and a very funny act it is, too. Cop, you have real talent. You should have become a clown long ago. Yessiree, I could tell by the way this boy was laughing it was really good. Say, who are you anyway, Boy?

COP (*Feebly*): Why, he's a friend of ours . . .

CLOWN (*Finishing*): Just popped up to say hello.

OWNER: Since he's a friend of yours, you won't object if I invite him to be my personal guest at the Big Top today, will you? I know he'll want to see the first performance of your new "Crying Clowns" act. Come along, son.

CLOWN: You mean we're to perform what we just did?

COP: Together? . . . Crying?

OWNER: Of course, of course, you just finished rehearsing it. In fact it is going to be such a huge success, I won't be a bit surprised if you get star billing on all the bill-boards. See you at the Big Top in half an hour. (*Putting his arm around the* BOY's *shoulder.*) First we have to get you some hot dogs and cotton candy and . . . (*They exit together while the* COP *and the* CLOWN *stare at each other in astonishment. Slowly the* COP *extends his hand for a handshake.*)

COP: Put 'er there, old buddy.

CLOWN: Old pal.

TOGETHER: I'm so happy I could cry. (*And they do, for joy. Out of the* CLOWN's *pocket, they pull a mammoth red hanky. They each use one corner of it to blow on. Across the hanky in large white letters appear the words: The End.*)

THE END

King John and the Abbot of Canterbury

by Ruth Vickery Holmes

Characters

SHEPHERD
KING JOHN
FIRST NOBLEMAN
SECOND NOBLEMAN
ABBOT OF CANTERBURY
REGENT OF CAMBRIDGE
REGENT OF OXFORD

SCENE 1

SETTING: *A country roadside.*

AT RISE: SHEPHERD *enters from left center, talking to his sheep offstage behind him.*

SHEPHERD (*Without looking back*): Come on now. If you stop to nibble at every green sprout on the road, I'll never reach the Abbey by nightfall. (KING JOHN *enters unnoticed behind the* SHEPHERD, *who speaks emphatically to his sheep, without looking behind him, but swinging his crook dangerously near* KING JOHN.) Get on

199

with you, I say. Or else you'll feel the prodding of my crook.

KING JOHN (*Sharply*) Are those words meant for me, Sirrah? Are you telling your King to *get on?*

SHEPHERD (*Turning toward* KING JOHN, *astonished at his presence there*): What? The King? (*Bowing low*) Your Majesty's pardon. I thought the sheep and I had the road to ourselves. I was but urging them to move faster. (FIRST *and* SECOND NOBLEMEN *enter, and stand respectfully behind the* KING.)

KING JOHN (*Turning to* FIRST NOBLEMAN. *In a sneering tone*): This varlet here wants the road to himself. He even suggests prodding his King with his sword.

SHEPHERD (*Protesting*): Indeed, your Majesty—I did not mean—I did not know—

KING JOHN (*Interrupting*): I go for a stroll while the horses rest. And a country oaf orders me to *get on*. He threatens to *prod me*. (*Turning toward* SECOND NOBLEMAN) What think you he deserves?

SECOND NOBLEMAN (*Stepping toward* SHEPHERD): Shall I run my blade through his heart?

FIRST NOBLEMAN (*Drawing close to* KING): Or does your Majesty wish him saved for hanging?

SHEPHERD (*Stepping backward*): Your Majesty, I entreat you to hear me. I was but trying to hurry my sheep. I promised to get them to the Abbey ere nightfall. The Abbot says that no sheep near Canterbury are so tender as mine.

KING JOHN (*Pacing back and forth in anger*): Ha! So your sheep are for the Abbot of Canterbury. Worse and worse. The tales that have been brought me of his arrogance!

SECOND NOBLEMAN (*Nodding*): His wealth is at fault. Such

gold as flows from his hands results naturally in arrogance and pride.

FIRST NOBLEMAN (*Going close to* KING): Yes. 'Tis the common report that a full hundred nobles feast with him each night.

KING JOHN (*Angrily*): He keeps court in grand style. With more lavish spending than his King contrives.

FIRST NOBLEMAN (*Nodding agreement*): Should any man in the land live better than the King?

KING JOHN (*Vigorously*): That no man shall do. The Abbot flies high. But I will trim his wings. (*Pauses to think, then steps toward* SHEPHERD.) To you I will be lenient. I will spare your life. Be off with you now. And say to the Abbot of Canterbury that he is summoned to our presence. Let him reach the court in three days time.

SHEPHERD (*Bowing*): My thanks, Your Majesty. (*Stepping forward sturdily*) But the Abbot. It was no fault of his, Your Majesty, that my sheep blocked Your Majesty's road.

KING JOHN (*With wrath*): Hold your tongue, man. Our business with the Abbot is in no way your concern. But your life, and his as well, will be the forfeit should he fail to reach our court in three days time.

CURTAIN

*   *   *

SCENE 2

SETTING: *Throne room in King John's palace.*
AT RISE: KING JOHN *is seated on throne facing audience.*

KING JOHN (*To* FIRST NOBLEMAN): So the Abbot has arrived, and waits to be received. Well, show him in.

FIRST NOBLEMAN (*Bowing*): As Your Majesty wishes. (*Goes out*)

SECOND NOBLEMAN (*Turning toward* KING): I'll wager that the trip to court was none to his liking. The hardships of the road would not be easy for one used to the comforts of Canterbury.

KING JOHN (*Nodding*): The comforts—humph—the luxury. Well, the Abbot may find that other details of this journey are none too much to his liking. (FIRST NOBLEMAN *enters, followed by the* ABBOT, *who bows low*.) Ah, so you're here, my good Abbot.

ABBOT (*Bowing again*): At your service, Your Majesty. As a loyal subject, I hastened to obey your summons.

KING JOHN (*Sneering*): As a *loyal* subject? Does a *loyal* subject live in such state that his daily banquets outdo in grandeur those at the court of his king?

ABBOT (*Stepping nearer to the throne*): O King, I do not know what the reports are that may have reached your ears, but I attempt no grandeur. I simply try to make life pleasant for my friends.

KING JOHN (*Sternly*): And you pour out gold with lavish hand in doing it.

ABBOT (*Firmly*): I provide only what I can well afford. I spend nothing but what is my own.

KING JOHN (*Leaning forward*): Then you have greater riches than your king. Should a loyal subject live better than his king? No, I say. No man in the land shall live better than the king.

ABBOT (*Drawing back*): I pray Your Majesty to think no ill of a subject who has had no wrong intent.

KING JOHN (*In anger*): Think no ill of a subject who puts his king to shame by living in grandeur greater than the royal court's? Perhaps you think that's suitable. No doubt you think that the Abbot of Canterbury is greater than the King of England.

ABBOT (*Emphatically*): Oh no, Your Majesty. No.

KING JOHN (*Interrupting with mounting anger*): Not another word. Your fault is plain. For such disloyalty your head should be cut off, and all your riches become mine.

ABBOT (*Advancing toward the throne*): But, Your Majesty, I do protest my innocence of evil intent. I crave your leniency.

KING JOHN (*Haughtily*): Your fault is plain, I say. You have assumed the right of royal grandeur. You are guilty of a grave offense. And yet you crave my leniency.

ABBOT (*Bowing*): As a subject whose every thought is loyal to his king, I crave your leniency and pardon.

SECOND NOBLEMAN (*Going close to* KING): Pardon, Your Majesty. But may I suggest—

KING JOHN (*Nodding to* FIRST NOBLEMAN, *then turns toward* ABBOT): I shall take a moment to reflect. That I am always fair and just is known to all. I will consider carefully before I make my sentence final. (ABBOT *turns, and goes slowly toward left, where he turns slowly, and stands with bowed head.* KING JOHN *and the two* NOBLEMEN *whisper together.*)

FIRST NOBLEMAN (*Audibly*): You see . . . Your Majesty's best interests would not be affected. But your generosity would be made plain.

KING JOHN (*Nodding, then leaning forward toward the* ABBOT.) You ask that I be lenient, and grant pardon.

ABBOT (*Drawing close to* KING): I do, O King.

KING JOHN (*Pleasantly*): Then I will, this time, be lenient.

ABBOT (*Fervently*): My humble thanks, your Majesty. My gratitude—

KING JOHN (*Interrupting*): But naturally, upon certain conditions.

ABBOT (*Taken aback*): Upon certain conditions?

KING JOHN (*Nodding*): Naturally, so grave an offense cannot be pardoned outright. But the conditions are generous. You have only to answer three questions. Then your life will be spared, and your estate remain yours.

ABBOT (*Warily*): May I ask what the questions are, Your Majesty? Gladly I'll answer your questions.

KING JOHN (*With solemnity*): Well, then. Here's the first question: As I sit here with my crown of gold on my head, you must tell me to within a day just how long I shall live.

ABBOT (*Protesting*): But, Your Majesty—

KING JOHN (*Firmly*): Next, you must tell me how soon I shall ride round the whole world.

ABBOT (*Shrugging his shoulders*): But Your Majesty knows that no man could answer—

KING JOHN (*Interrupting*): And lastly, you shall tell me what I think.

ABBOT (*Distressed*): Is it in human power to read the mind of another? (*Pauses, bowing his head in thought, then looks up slowly.*) If the answering of these questions is beyond my power, what then?

KING JOHN (*Nodding*): Then, naturally, the forfeit must be paid—your life and your riches.

ABBOT (*Despondent*): Ah, Your Majesty, I see—I see what you mean.

KING JOHN (*With sternness*): Do you, or do you not, accept the condition?

ABBOT (*Gathering courage*): I accept, Your Majesty. But to one so generous in his leniency, I make this request. To questions so profound, to questions that concern Your

Majesty's own person, it would not be in order to give unstudied answers. I beg for two weeks time. Then I'll return, and give such answers as I can.

KING JOHN (*Turning to* SECOND NOBLEMAN): Would such delay be overmuch, do you think? Shall we grant the Abbot two weeks time?

FIRST NOBLEMAN (*Bowing*): Two weeks will not, I think, affect the outcome to His Majesty's disfavor. Let the Abbot have his two weeks.

KING JOHN (*To* ABBOT): It is our pleasure, to answer favorably. Your request is granted. In two weeks time, return and give the answers. Fail not to be present here in two weeks time.

CURTAIN

*   *   *

SCENE 3

SETTING: *A room in the Abbey. Furnished simply with a table surrounded by chairs.*

AT RISE: THE ABBOT *is seated behind the table,* THE REGENT OF CAMBRIDGE *at the right end of the table, and* THE REGENT OF OXFORD, *at the left end.*

ABBOT (*Sighing*): Then in all Cambridge, no help could be found?

REGENT OF CAMBRIDGE (*Nodding*): No answers to such questions as the King's are possible, my lord. Our most noted scholars all agree to that.

ABBOT (*Turning to* THE REGENT OF OXFORD): And your report, too, is the same? Was there no one at Oxford who could solve them?

REGENT OF OXFORD (*Gravely*): Indeed, my lord, we scholars of Oxford are in agreement. The questions put to you by the King *cannot* be answered.

ABBOT (*Despondently*): That, I acknowledge, is doubtless his intent. The questions are unanswerable. When I start back to court tomorrow, no hope goes with me. I fear my life has nearly run its course.

SHEPHERD (*Entering from right, and bowing*): Your pardon, my lord. You have helped me these long years past. Now I've come to help you. I beg leave to take your trouble from your back, and bear it on my own.

ABBOT (*Looking up, surprised*): Those are brave words. But have you knowledge of what confronts me?

SHEPHERD (*Nodding*): Ay, my lord. I know full well. I know the condition made by the King for your pardon. It is a sentence of death, in a manner of speaking. But I know, too, how to save you. Let the whole matter be simply a jest. . . .

ABBOT (*Drawing himself up, annoyed*): Your concern, if concern it is, makes your words sound like a fool's.

SHEPHERD (*Stepping nearer*): But, my lord, have you never heard that a fool may teach a wise man wit? Have all the scholars of Cambridge and of Oxford, or your own scholars here in Canterbury, met with success? What help has come from them?

REGENT OF CAMBRIDGE (*Interrupting*): None, by my faith. No help at all.

SHEPHERD (*Turning, and nodding*): The good sir bears me out. The questions put you by the King were naught but jests, most cruel jests. Well then. As fire puts out fire, so meet jest with jest.

ABBOT (*Nodding*): Go on. Wisdom, perhaps, is the real root of what I took for folly. Tell me what you have planned.

SHEPHERD (*Leaning upon the table*): Lend me your horse and gown, and servants to go with me. A false beard, too, must be upon my chin. Then I, as the Abbot of Canterbury, will keep the tryst in London.

ABBOT (*Surprised*): Where, as Abbot of Canterbury, you are likely to die. A good friend you are to call that a jest.

SHEPHERD (*Firmly*): And is my life of such account as yours? But there are other jests I've thought of. The answers to the questions. There is a chance—such jests as mine perchance might win the day.

REGENT OF OXFORD (*Nodding to* ABBOT): If the fellow's wit matches the stoutness of his heart, the day may yet be saved. I'll ride in his train to see his courage put to action.

REGENT OF CAMBRIDGE (*Agreeing*): And so will I. And I pray Heaven that all goes well.

SHEPHERD (*Bows to express his thanks, then faces* ABBOT): But if worst comes to worst, I will die in your place.

ABBOT (*With decision*): No. That you'll not. I too, will ride in your train, concealed in your cloak and hood. But if worst comes to worst, I will die for myself.

CURTAIN

*   *   *

SCENE 4

SETTING: *Same as Scene 2.*

AT RISE: KING JOHN *sits on throne.* FIRST NOBLEMAN *and* SECOND NOBLEMAN *stand behind center.* SHEPHERD, *disguised as* ABBOT, *stands facing* KING JOHN.

KING JOHN (*Sneering*): Welcome, Sir Abbot, welcome. Just two weeks to the day since your last visit. (SHEPHERD *bows.*)

FIRST NOBLEMAN (*With sarcasm*): The Abbot has, no doubt, spent the full two weeks studying His Majesty's questions.

SHEPHERD (*Bowing*): Ay. With most careful consideration.

SECOND NOBLEMAN (*With derision*): And, no doubt, with his careful consideration, the Abbot has found answers to all the questions.

SHEPHERD (*Bowing*): Ay. Answers to all the three questions.

KING JOHN (*Nettled*): Indeed. Indeed. And you know that failure to answer will cost you your life? You must ask no more leniency of me. A bargain's a bargain, and should be kept fair and square. All the world may bear witness that I'm always fair.

SHEPHERD (*Bowing*): Thank you, Your Majesty, for so proper a suggestion.

KING JOHN (*Astonished*): Suggestion? What suggestion did I make?

SHEPHERD (*Bowing*): But we need hardly call on all the world to bear witness in this case. Sufficient it will be to have present the three friends who came with me. May they be summoned here, Your Majesty?

KING JOHN (*In anger*): What, sir? Did you bring witnesses?

FIRST NOBLEMAN (*Drawing close to* KING): Your Majesty's title to the Abbey will be the better established. And the justice of the sentence more plainly proved.

KING JOHN (*Dubiously*): True. Entirely true. Let the Abbot's friends be summoned. (FIRST NOBLEMAN *goes out left*.) Your three friends—all the world—it matters not to me who bears witness.

FIRST NOBLEMAN (*Entering from left, followed by* THE REGENT OF CAMBRIDGE, THE REGENT OF OXFORD, *and the* ABBOT, *disguised in* SHEPHERD's *cloak and hood*): Your Majesty, the Regent of Cambridge. (*He bows.*) The Regent of Oxford. (*He bows.*) And the simple Shepherd you saw once before. (*He bows.*)

KING JOHN (*Leaning forward*): Ah ha, the Shepherd. Well, no more ado. Our business must proceed. Now then, Sir Abbot. It is understood. If you fail to answer my three questions, you shall lose your head, and your wealth shall be mine.

SHEPHERD (*Nodding assent*): And if, Your Majesty, I give you answers, then my life is to be spared, and my estate remain my own.

KING JOHN (*Turning to look at the witnesses*): Yes, that is the bargain as it stands. (*To* SHEPHERD) Now then. The questions. Tell me, Sir Abbot, to the day, *How Long Shall I Live?*

SHEPHERD (*Slowly, with great solemnity*): You shall live until the day that you die, and not one day longer. And you shall die when you take your last breath, and not one moment before.

KING JOHN (*Baffled and uncertain*): You are witty, indeed. But we will let that pass, and say that your answer is right. And now tell me this: *How Soon May I Ride Round the Whole World?*

SHEPHERD (*Profoundly*): You must rise with the sun, and you must ride with the sun until it rises again the next morning. As soon as you do that, you will find that you have ridden round the whole world in twenty-four hours.

KING JOHN (*Smiling with reluctance*): Indeed, Sir Abbot, you are not only witty, you are wise. I had not myself thought that so long a journey could take so little time.

(*Then leaning forward, sternly*) But enough. As you value your life, no more jesting. Tell me this if you can. *What Do I Think?*

SHEPHERD (*Pauses, as if lost in thought; then stepping forward*): You *think,* Your Majesty, you *think*—that I am the Abbot of Canterbury.

KING JOHN (*In triumph*) : Ha, I *know* it. Knowing is not the same as thinking. You've not told me what I *think.*

SHEPHERD (*Interrupting*): But, Your Majesty, look. (*Throws off gown and pulls the beard away*) Not the Abbot am I. But only his shepherd. (KING JOHN *laughs in spite of himself, then laughs more loudly, and all present join in.* SHEPHERD *steps nearer the throne.*) Forgive me, Your Majesty. I came in the hope that the Abbot would be saved. A bargain's a bargain.

KING (*Breaking in*): Which I'll keep fair and square as all can bear witness. Your wit has served both you and the Abbot. Four pieces of silver each week shall be yours your life long.

SHEPHERD (*Bowing*): My thanks, Your Majesty. But the Abbot? Do you pardon the Abbot?

KING (*Turns and looks at the witnesses; then turns to look at each* NOBLEMAN; *then nods slowly*): For the Abbot, a free pardon from the King.

THE END

The Runaway Pirate

by Rowena Bennett

Characters

PIRATE
STEAMSHIP CAPTAIN
SUBMARINE OFFICER
AIRPLANE PILOT
SAILORS

SETTING: *A harbor.*

AT RISE: *The* PIRATE *is strutting about stage, puffing out his chest and twirling his mustache. The other characters are seated on kegs, benches, or on the floor around him.*

PIRATE: Oh, I am a pirate in search of a crew,
   And a nice tidy ship to go sailing in, too.
   I'm tough and I'm rough and there's naught I won't do
   For a ship and a crew—
   For some bold buccaneers with rings in their ears,
   And a cutlass or two. (*He does a jig.*)
   I'm tough and I'm rough and I'm used to the sea,
   And I want some brave boys to go sailing with me.
   (*He shades his eyes with his hand and studies crowd.*)

You all look like dudes . . . but *that* fellow may do. (*He points.*)

I'll toughen him up . . . and you, sir, and you. (*He indicates two others.*)

CAPTAIN (*Rising*): Are you really a pirate? A man of the sea?

OFFICER (*Also rising*): And you want for your crew men like me?

PILOT (*Also rising*): And like me?

PIRATE: Of course. And I'll teach you the ways of a ship.

THREE MEN: That's kind of you, brother. We need a good tip. (*They burst into laughter.*)

PIRATE: I'll teach you to handle a rope and a sail.

We'll travel so fast that we'll be out of hail

By tonight . . . or tomorrow . . .

CAPTAIN (*Almost choking on a chuckle*): Good gracious! What speed!

OFFICER (*Winking at* CAPTAIN *and* PILOT): This kind of instruction is just what we need.

PILOT (*Aside in puzzled voice to* CAPTAIN *and* OFFICER): This fellow has stepped from a picture or dream . . .

CAPTAIN: He's not seen a smokestack, or engine, or steam.

OFFICER (*To* PIRATE): Just where did you come from, my buccaneer hearty?

PILOT: From carnival? Circus?

CAPTAIN: Or masquerade party? (*They laugh.*)

PIRATE (*Angrily, hand on cutlass*): You'd better not scoff in contemptuous tones.

Behold the black flag with its skull and cross bones.

(*He takes his pirate flag from his pocket and shakes it in their faces. They back away a little.*)

OTHERS: The banner that only a true pirate owns! (*They look impressed*)

PIRATE: I've come from the locker of old *Davy Jones.*

OTHERS (*Shuddering a little*): The undersea locker of old Davy Jones?

PIRATE (*Confidentially in stage whisper*): I gave him the slip. Old Davy was sleeping.

I slid from his grip and out of his keeping.

I wanted a trip

In a nice tidy ship.

OTHERS: You were really quite brave

To rise from the grave.

PILOT (*Bowing to* PIRATE): Perhaps we can find you a ship, noble sir.

OFFICER (*Warningly*): It won't be the kind that old pirates prefer.

CAPTAIN (*Pointing out to sea on backdrop*): There goes the *Queen Mary.* Perhaps you'd like *her.*

PIRATE (*Looking aghast*): What? Is that a ship? Why! It hasn't a sail!

CAPTAIN: It travels by steam and without any gale. (*He hands the* PIRATE *a spy glass through which to look.*)

OFFICER: It's a hundred times bigger out there on the seas

Than it looks to you now, through such glasses as these.

(*He taps the spy glass*)

PIRATE: A ship run by steam? That was only a dream

When I was last here.

(*He looks through spy glass, and almost drops it.*)

Smoke! I see smoke! It's burning, I fear.

(*Whistle is blown loudly offstage.* PIRATE *jumps, drops glass, puts his hands to his ears, and hides behind keg.*)

CAPTAIN (*Winking at others*): Such a bold buccaneer! He is holding his ear.

PILOT (*Laughing*): He's the picture of fear.

OFFICER: Hey, Pirate, come here.

PILOT: That was only a whistle.

PIRATE (*Coming out*): It sounded too near. (*His knees are trembling.*)

A whistle like that! It would soon drive me daft!

What else do you have in a good sailing craft?

I want something small. Something tidy and neat.

Not a boat that's the size of an overgrown fleet.

OFFICER (*Looking through spy glass*): Well, there's something smaller. It's painted in green

With ripples of blue . . . (*He passes the spy glass to the* PIRATE.)

PIRATE (*Looking through glass*): It can barely be seen.

OFFICER: It's well camouflaged.

PIRATE (*Bewildered*): I don't know what you mean.

PILOT: He means it's a *sub* . . .

OFFICER: Yes. A war submarine.

PIRATE: Help! Help! It is sinking! (*He jumps up and down excitedly, dropping the spy glass.*)

OFFICER (*Trying to quiet him*): No, no, it's submerging.

PIRATE (*Running around in circles with his hands over his eyes*): I can't bear to look!

OFFICER (*To* CAPTAIN *and* PILOT):

He'll need more than urging.

We'll just *make* him look . . . where the waters are surging.

CAPTAIN: I'll grab him. (*He grabs the* PIRATE.)

PILOT: I'll hold him. (*He holds the struggling* PIRATE.)

OFFICER (*Taking the* PIRATE's *hands from his eyes*): I'll pin down his hands.

CAPTAIN (*Picking up spy glass and putting it to the* PIRATE's *eye*): I'll hold up this glass, till the man understands.

PIRATE (*Still breathless, looking*):

Look! Now it comes up! That ship is a wonder.

It travels the ocean, both over and under.

OTHERS: That's just what we mean when we say *Sub-marine.*

PIRATE (*Aghast*): But I *couldn't* run that ship.

I just couldn't dock her.

Besides she would take me

To Davy Jones' Locker.

I have *just* come from there

To breathe nice salty air

And to find me a ship

That will answer my prayer.

OTHERS: Very well, there will soon be another ship coming.

PILOT: There's one coming now! Don't you all hear that humming? (*He looks up. An airplane is heard.*)

PIRATE (*Crouching and trembling at the noise*): What a noise! What a scare!

Another ship? Where?

OTHERS (*Pointing out over the sea*): Out there! In the air!

PIRATE (*Peeking out from behind keg*): What? A ship that has wings?

Why! Of all the strange things! (*He starts to creep away, still trembling*)

But a man such as I

Doesn't know how to fly . . .

And I don't think I'll try. (*He is almost offstage now.*)

OTHERS (*Looking around*): Here! Where are you going? Your feet getting cold?

PIRATE (*Standing up shakily and bursting into tears*): I'm a pirate, just think! I am seasoned and old,

With ducats that clink and ear-rings of gold.
I'm a pirate, just think! I'm a buccaneer bold!
But I'm 'fraid you are right. My feet have turned cold.
(*He sobs loudly.*)
I just couldn't navigate engines of steam,
Nor fly through the ether and stay on the beam.
I just couldn't make any rudder behave
If I had to sail *under* the billowy wave.
I'm not at all brave. (*He wails loudly.*)
When I'm back with Davy I'll surely be glad.
It just didn't pay to run off and be bad. (*He runs off sniffling. The others look after him, then turn and look at one another.*)

CAPTAIN: Poor fellow! He hasn't a brag or a boast
Left on his tongue . . .

OFFICER: He'll find his old post
In Davy Jones' Locker the thing he likes most.

PILOT (*Smiling*): He *isn't* a pirate. He's only a ghost.

THE END

Home, Sweet Home

by Sally Werner

Characters

PEEK, *a little mouse*
TIPTOE, *another mouse*
MUSKRAT
PORCUPINE
RABBIT
MOLE
SPARROWS

SETTING: *A barnyard.*
AT RISE: PEEK *and* TIPTOE *are sitting side by side, chins in hands.*

PEEK: Look here Tiptoe, this barn of ours is much too far from the corn crib. It seems we could find a better place to live, where food would be much handier. (*Looking around*) It's getting a bit old-fashioned looking, too.
TIPTOE: You are right, Peek—so right. Let us be off to look for a better place before it is too late. (*Mice tie a few belongings in red kerchiefs.*)
PEEK: It takes us quite a while to pack. We've lived here for some time, you know.

217

TIPTOE: Yes, I know. But that's no reason why we can't look for a better place. (*They tie bundles to end of sticks as* SPARROWS *enter, chattering to each other.*)

1ST SPARROW: My goodness, what goes on here?

2ND SPARROW: Where are you going?

3RD SPARROW: What's all the packing for?

PEEK: If you'll just keep still for a moment we'll tell you. We are going to find a new home. A modern home, new and different.

TIPTOE: Where food is easier to find.

4TH SPARROW: Food?

5TH SPARROW: Easier to find?

PEEK *and* TIPTOE: That's right. Goodbye sparrows. (*Start off. Walk about stage, looking around*)

1ST SPARROW: How do you like that? Those silly mice.

2ND SPARROW: They don't know when they're well off. Why there's plenty of food right here. (SPARROWS *leave, chattering about mice.* MUSKRAT *enters near mice.*)

MUSKRAT: Good morning, mice. What are you doing out here?

PEEK: We are looking for a new home. We need something new and different before the cold weather sets in.

TIPTOE: Something snug and warm.

MUSKRAT: Well! You are just the ones I've been looking for. I have just started building my house and I do need help. When we have finished, you will like my house and you can live with me.

TIPTOE: We-ll—all right, muskrat. I'll help you.

PEEK: So will I.

MUSKRAT: Fine, fine. (*Briskly*) Now then, come along with me. We have work to do. (MUSKRAT *and mice leave and re-appear carrying bundles across stage, dis-*

*appear and re-appear again. Each time the mice walk
slower and slower.)*

TIPTOE (*As they appear again with twigs*): Peek, let's go
on. I don't think we'd like to live with muskrat. I don't
want to build a house.

PEEK: I was just thinking the same thing. (*They throw
twigs down.*) Here comes porcupine. (PORCUPINE *enters.*)

PORCUPINE: Good morning, mice. What are you doing out
here?

PEEK: Good morning, porcupine. We are looking for a
new home, something comfortable and warm before the
cold weather sets in.

TIPTOE: And we're very hungry.

PORCUPINE: Hungry? Ah, my dear friends, I was just hop-
ing someone like you would come along. I have a feast—
a grand feast—if you will only come with me to help
carry it. We can eat right here.

PEEK: You are so kind, porcupine. Of course we will come
to help you. (*They leave and return with a large board.*)

PORCUPINE: There. Let's put it right down here. Weren't
we lucky to find this nice weathered board.

TIPTOE: What are we going to put on this table, porcupine?

PORCUPINE: Table? (*Laughs*) Oh, my dear mice. This is
no table. This is our dinner. A good weathered board.
Mmm, what could be nicer. Sit right over there. I'll take
this end.

PEEK: But we can't, you see we don't eat wood.

TIPTOE: Oh, we gnaw it once in a while, but we don't
really eat it, you know.

PORCUPINE: Hmmm, I just can't understand it. And you

said you were hungry. Well, in that case I won't sit and eat here in front of you. I'll go down to the hollow. (*Picks up board*) Sorry, mice. See you later.

PEEK: My goodness, what shall we do now?

TIPTOE: Here comes rabbit. (RABBIT *enters.*)

RABBIT: Hello mice. What are you doing way out here?

TIPTOE: Hello rabbit. We are looking for a new home. The north wind is getting very cold.

RABBIT: So it is. Well now, let me think. It just happens that one of my relations—don't remember which one— I have so many, but one of them moved out of his house under that old stump the other day. I wouldn't call it a fancy place, but winter is coming and you must have a home. You're welcome to it. One can't be too choosey you know.

PEEK: Thank you, Rabbit.

RABBIT: Not at all. (RABBIT *leaves.*)

PEEK: Well, we might as well go in. (*They crawl under chairs and come out on other side which is underground. They stay on knees.*)

TIPTOE: My goodness, Peek, do you think we could ever make this place look homey?

PEEK: Dear me—no. And we could never keep the cupboard filled. There's just nothing here but some old roots. Let's move on. (*They creep wrong way.*)

TIPTOE: Is this the way? It looks like the wrong tunnel. (MOLE *comes creeping in to meet them.*)

MOLE: Well, I do believe it is two mice. It is a bit difficult to see in this tunnel. You are mice, aren't you?

PEEK: Hello, Mole. Glad you came along. Yes, we are mice and we are lost. You see we are looking for a new home before winter sets in. Rabbit offered us this, but we can't live here.

TIPTOE: This is no place for mice.

MOLE: Well now, fancy that. I came just in time because winter is just about here. It so happens that I know of a very nice house that you might occupy. Two mice lived there once, but for some silly reason they left. I heard some sparrows talking about them. I just happened to run into this house on one of my travels. If you will follow me, I'll lead the way. (*They start creeping about stage.*)

PEEK: Is it an underground dwelling, Mole?

MOLE: Oh no. You see I can never find my way around up there on top. I always go by underground method. I can always find my way through these tunnels. Let's see now—you turn south here—and now you angle off southwest. (*Creep about in all directions,* MOLE *leading the way. Finally end up at the barn in the corner where mice first lived*) There it is right above us. This is where we go up. Here's a hole in the floor. (*Mice look around barn and at corn crib*)

TIPTOE: A wonderful place! And look, a corn crib. It is a long time since we had a good meal. Oh, Peek, I like this! I've been so lonesome for our old barn and this looks like . . . (*Looks around*)

PEEK: It is a nice warm, comfortable place. It reminds me so much of the place where we once lived—so much! (*Looks around*)

TIPTOE: Yes, but it looks much better now, doesn't it?

PEEK: Then, it is? Of course it is. It's our barn, Tiptoe.

TIPTOE: Yes. (*Sighs happily*) Oh, thank you, Mole, for taking us home.

MOLE: Then you are the two mice I heard the sparrows mention?

PEEK *and* TIPTOE: Yes, yes! Thank you, Mole.

MOLE: Not at all, not at all. I know just how you feel. (*Briskly*) Well, I really must move along. Working on a new tunnel right now. Goodbye.

PEEK *and* TIPTOE: Goodbye, Mole. (MOLE *leaves.* SPARROWS *enter chattering.*)

1ST SPARROW: Why hello, mice, Glad to see you.

TIPTOE: Hello, Sparrows. It's good to see you again.

2ND SPARROW: And how did you come out on your travels?

PEEK: Fine, Sparrows, just fine.

TIPTOE: Yes, indeed. We found there's no place like home.

3RD SPARROW: Well, it pays to look around.

MICE: It certainly does. (*They smile happily at each other.*)

THE END

The Fortune of Merrylegs and Tawny-Whiskers

by Lida Lisle Molloy

Characters

MERRYLEGS, *a lad*
TAWNY-WHISKERS, *a wise cat*
BAKER
APPRENTICES
INNKEEPER
TOWN CRIER
BREW MASTER
SERVING MEN
SCHOOLMASTER

SETTING: *An old inn.*

AT RISE: MERRYLEGS *is seated tailor-fashion before the blackened fireplace, twirling a bright piece of silver on the floor.* TAWNY-WHISKERS *lies nearby, his head resting on his forepaws. A bell rings merrily without.*

TOWN CRIER (*Ringing and chanting*): What ho! Let it be known that one, Merrylegs, a lad of good parts, and his Cat, Tawny-Whiskers, have this day come into a fortune, having found a sixpence of silver under a white-thorn hedge. If there be any man of wit and understanding who can bestow sound advice upon the investments of moneys, let him haste to appear at Wayfarer's Inn. (*The ringing and chanting grow less distinct until they are heard no more.*) What ho! etc. . . .

MERRYLEGS (*Listening with pleasure*): Hist! (*Twists an ear of the sleeping* TAWNY-WHISKERS.) Do you hear? (*The* CAT *raises his head slowly.*) I am Merrylegs and you are Tawny-Whiskers, and the Crier is telling all the world that we have found a sixpence as silver as the moon. (*"Meow" proudly admits the* CAT.) Now, my friend, when men of learning come to tell us how we may best employ our wealth, do you listen well. You who have been the Royal Mouse-Catcher and have sat upon the Queen's footstool know the ways of the world as, alas, I cannot. Do you then, when the advice of a man pleases you, purr gently under your breath—like this— (*Attempts to make a purring sound that is taken up by the* CAT.) That is it—as soft as ever a small wind sounds. Then, if a man's words please you but moderately, pitch your voice a little louder. (*The* CAT *demonstrates.*) And if he please you not at all, scold and rage furiously. (*The* CAT *spits and hisses angrily. The* LAD *claps his hands.*) Merry! You will be a splendid counselor! (*Footsteps are heard without.*) P-s-st! (*Finger to lips.*) Men of fortune must bear themselves with dignity.

BAKER (*Shouting without*): Innkeeper, I would see Master Merrylegs. (*The* CAT *and* LAD *nudge each other.*)

INNKEEPER (*Without*): Step within, good Baker. Step within. (*The* BAKER *comes in with a flourish. He carries a huge beating spoon. After him hurry two panting* APPRENTICES, *each carrying a large tray above his head.*

One tray is filled with long, flat loaves of bread and the other with sweet rolls and tarts. The BAKER *makes a low bow.*)

BAKER: Master Merrylegs! (MERRYLEGS *jumps nimbly to his feet, doffs his feather-tipped hat and bows.*)

MERRYLEGS: Your honor!

BAKER: You are a man of moneys, Master Merrylegs.

MERRYLEGS: Yes, good Baker. I and my wise companion, Tawny-Whiskers . . . (*Takes the paw of the* CAT *who rises and bows politely*) . . . were but seeking under the white-thorn hedge for late strawberries when we came upon this goodly silver sixpence. (*Holds up the money. The* APPRENTICES *gape with envy.*)

BAKER: Silver! Ah! I have not seen the like since His Majesty, the King, having lost himself in the hunting of a deer, did stop to buy . . . (*He carefully folds down a finger as he mentions each item*) . . . six venison pastries, a dozen and three gooseberry tartlets, a pot of fine quince jam and a stick of candied ginger.

MERRYLEGS (*Impressed*): How wise you must be since you have served the King. Can you not tell us how best to invest our riches?

BAKER (*Bowing*) : With pleasure, young sir. (*To the* APPRENTICES.) Approach, Flax-head, Light-wit! (*The two* APPRENTICES *come forward, kneel on right knee and lower their trays before* MERRYLEGS.) Behold, Master Merrylegs, I have spread before you what every man must have—food. Though a man be a beggar and sleep under a green tree, yet if he have a loaf he may be content.

MERRYLEGS: It is most uncomfortable not to have a loaf. (*Sighing*) Is it not, Tawny-Whiskers? (*The* CAT *nods gravely.*)

BAKER: Let me advise you, gentles, (*Bowing*) to change your fortune into food—brown loaves warm and crackling from the oven, raspberry tarts dainty enough for the mouth of a princess.

MERRYLEGS (*Wistfully*): I have not so much as tasted a tart, good Tawny-Whiskers, since the day I was seven and my mother made one with mulberry jam. (*At a sign from the* BAKER, *the* APPRENTICE *with the tray of tarts approaches closer to the* LAD.) How many will you trade for our silver sixpence?

BAKER: Three long loaves of bread and a half-dozen tarts, my good lad. (*The* CAT *begins to "meow" loudly. Hastily the* BAKER *adds*) Ah! I will make it a round dozen of the tarts—a dozen, and add a honey cake for good measure. (*The* CAT *continues to "meow."*)

MERRYLEGS: But look you, honest Baker, when the feasting were done we would have neither food nor sixpence, and Tawny-Whiskers must take to catching mice again for his bowl of milk and I to skimming cream for my curds. It seems it were best to go on catching and skimming . . . (*The* BREW MASTER *comes rushing in.*)

BREW MASTER: Master Merrylegs!

MERRYLEGS: Here, good sir.

BREW MASTER (*Anxiously*): Have you done away with the silver sixpence?

MERRYLEGS: No, indeed, friend. 'Tis not under every hedgerow one may pick up a fortune. (*The disgruntled* BAKER *and his* APPRENTICES *leave.*)

BREW MASTER (*Rubbing his hands together*): Ah! What an extraordinary lad you are! (*Calling*) Trundle in, my men! Trundle in! (*Two men appear rolling a small barrel. They stand in front of the* BOY *and step back.*)

What a wise lad you are! You have been waiting for the
barrel.

MERRYLEGS: What is in it?

BREW MASTER: Ale, Master Merrylegs.

MERRYLEGS (*Uncertainly*): What is Ale?

BREW MASTER: Ho! Ho! I must introduce you. Master
Merrylegs, Master Ale. (BREW MASTER *points to the
barrel. The* LAD *bows with an air of bewilderment.*) A
very pretty bow, young sir, but you will bend to him
with more grace when you know him better. (*He winks
openly at the* SERVING MEN; *they nudge each other and
say,* "Ho! ho!")

MERRYLEGS: Is Master Ale within the barrel?

BREW MASTER: Indeed! All you have to do is to draw the
wooden stopper from the end and out it pours . . .

MERRYLEGS: Oh, is he a genie? Does he rush out like a
great cloud and thunder, "I am the slave of the barrel.
What is your command?"

BREW MASTER: Genie he is, clever lad, though he does not
come forth in a cloud. Instead he is a potion for men to
drink. You pour him into a tankard! You lift him to
your lips! Ah! Soon he begins to work . . . magic.

MERRYLEGS: Magic! Do you hear that, Tawny-Whiskers?
(*The* CAT *is beginning to make deep, angry noises in
his throat.*) This magic, would it bring us gold enough
to pay the money lender, so that we might buy again
the cottage of my father?

BREW MASTER: No! no! It is a much stronger magic, young
sir. Drink Master Ale, and if you are cold he will make
you feel warm as any crackling fire. If you are hungry—
it will be as though you had feasted at the King's table.
If you are penniless—a lord with a thousand silk-clad

retainers will not feel as rich as you. All this may be yours, wise Merrylegs, if you buy the barrel with the sixpence of silver.

MERRYLEGS (*Puzzled*): But if I am still cold and hungry and beggared even though I *feel* I am not, what poor kind of magic would that be? (*The* CAT *moves toward the* BREW MASTER *who begins to back away cautiously.*)

BREW MASTER (*Backing away*): You do not understand, Master Merrylegs. (*Still backing away*) You do not . . . (*Enter* SCHOOLMASTER.)

SCHOOLMASTER: Weladay, Brew Master! Up to your roguery again. Did I not tell you the next time I saw you enticing the young with your poison I would plant a staff on your head?

BREW MASTER (*Trembling*): I am going, honored Schoolmaster.

SCHOOLMASTER: 'Twere best, else I might lose my reputation as a man of peace and thwack you roundly. (*The* BREW MASTER *leaves hurriedly, followed by the two* MEN *with the barrel.* SCHOOLMASTER *stands looking after him, twirling his staff.* MERRYLEGS *approaches him and timidly pulls his sleeve.*)

MERRYLEGS: Good sir, was Master Ale a rogue?

SCHOOLMASTER: Something of a rogue, young Master Merrylegs. He carries no magic, only a sly poison that often robs men of wit and wealth.

MERRYLEGS: Oh-h!

SCHOOLMASTER: Fret you not; he is gone. You still have your sixpence of silver and a goodly lesson to crown it withal.

MERRYLEGS (*To the* CAT): It is sad, good Tawny-Whiskers, to be people of fortune. Before we came upon this sixpence rogues did not seek our company.

SCHOOLMASTER: What! Sad to be a man of fortune? Never! I know a thousand splendid things a clever lad and a cat might do with a sixpence.

MERRYLEGS: Name one, sir.

SCHOOLMASTER: A lad might buy a book . . .

MERRYLEGS: A book? (*Here the* CAT *begins to purr as gently as any "small wind."*)

SCHOOLMASTER (*Opening the big book he carries*): . . . a book wherein he would learn how wondrously this world is made. (*Turning the pages while* MERRYLEGS *stands on tiptoe watching.*) Would you know how the moon pulls up the tides? What manner of men live on the other side of the earth? Where swallows fly when winter blows cold? 'Tis all to be found in books.

MERRYLEGS (*Wistfully*): My good father meant I should be a man of learning, honored schoolmaster, but I was scarce beyond the alphabet when he and my mother died.

SCHOOLMASTER: Is there any law writ which says you may not still be a man of learning? All that it takes, Master Merrylegs, is a boy and a Will to Learn. But I must not tarry. A score of lads wait in my garden to learn how coral palaces are built in the sea. Fare you well! Good day, and good fortune attend you, Master Merrylegs! Master Tawny-Whiskers! (*They bow to each other, but he has scarcely turned to go when* MERRYLEGS *is after him.*)

MERRYLEGS (*Eagerly*): The book, good sir. Would you trade the book for the silver sixpence?

SCHOOLMASTER (*Turning*): The book? Ah! Would you care for it well? I vow no man should own a book who does not love it better than his life.

MERRYLEGS: Schoolmaster, when it rains the book shall

have half my cloak, and if Tawny-Whiskers and I find no lodgings it shall sleep between us in the fields.

SCHOOLMASTER: The book is yours, Lad.

MERRYLEGS (*Bowing many times*): A thousand thousand thanks, honored sir. (*Runs to* TAWNY-WHISKERS. *The* SCHOOLMASTER *starts to leave the room and then turns back to stand by the left wall and watch the pair.*) Tawny-Whiskers, have you a Will to Learn? (*They sit on the floor, peeping into the book.*)

INNKEEPER (*Cautiously*): Master Merrylegs! Master Merrylegs!

MERRYLEGS: Here, good Innkeeper.

INNKEEPER (*Poking his head in the door*): Master Merrylegs, are you alone? The baker has returned with a fine basket of cinnamon buns (*Smacking his lips*) which he says is worth any man's fortune.

MERRYLEGS (*With dignity*): Bid Master Baker peddle his wares in the market place, innkeeper. Tawny-Whiskers and I have traded our sixpence for a Will to Learn.

SCHOOLMASTER (*Making himself known with a hearty laugh*): Bravo!

MERRYLEGS (*Surprised*): Schoolmaster!

SCHOOLMASTER (*Gravely*): Merrylegs, I have discovered that my cottage needs a boy and a cat. The mice are becoming far too impudent; they nibble at my cheeses. (TAWNY-WHISKERS *waggles his head.*) And my garden walks are quite disgraceful. I must have a lad about to remind me to sweep them daily.

MERRYLEGS: Would Tawny-Whiskers and I do, sir?

SCHOOLMASTER: If you find the catnip in my herb bed to your liking and my barley cake and curds. (*Twinkling*) Shall we form a trial partnership?

MERRYLEGS: Please, sir.

TAWNY-WHISKERS: Meow! Meow!

SCHOOLMASTER: Then let us upon our way. There will be twenty lads . . .

MERRYLEGS: One and twenty lads, sir.

SCHOOLMASTER: Quite right. There will be one and twenty lads in the garden, Master Merrylegs, all waiting to learn . . .

MERRYLEGS: . . . how coral castles are built in the sea! (*Confidentially to the* CAT) What if we had traded our fortune for buns instead of a book and a Will to Learn, Tawny-Whiskers!

TAWNY-WHISKERS: Meow! Meow! (*They run out together.*)

THE END

Production Notes

FINAL EDITION

Characters: 8 male.

Playing Time: 30 minutes.

Costumes: Everyday, modern dress. The reporters may work in shirts. Jimmy may wear a sweater or sport shirt. When Hank first enters, he wears a top coat. He takes off the coat and puts on a worn alpaca office coat. Welch and Simpson wear business suits.

Properties: Copy paper, pencils, pads, sheets of proof, sandwich wrapped in paper, cup of coffee, two white marbles, paper knife, newspapers, worn telephone book, personal belongings and books in Hank's desk.

Setting: The editorial room of a metropolitan newspaper. There are five battered desks in the room. Each desk holds a typewriter and a telephone. The desks are covered with copy paper, pencils, clippings and newspapers. The floor is littered with cuttings and miscellaneous papers which have missed the wastebaskets. At right is a door bearing the inscription: ROBERT WELCH—*Managing Editor.* On the left are swinging doors which lead to an entrance hallway. Upstage is a large window through which can be seen a view of the city. Also upstage, to the right, are the teletype machine, a telegraph instrument and the fire signal. At left is a coat rack holding some top coats, suit coats and Hank's office coat. Near the rack is a water cooler, and tacked on the wall behind the cooler are some photographs of glamorous movie stars.

Lighting: No special effects.

FIRES AT VALLEY FORGE

Characters: 9 male.

Playing Time: 30 minutes.

Costumes: Except for the corporal, who wears a rag around his head and rags on his feet, the players appear in their ordinary clothes.

Properties: A simulated old-fashioned musket; staffs for the boys, one with a bundle attached to it; sacks; knitted shawl; bread; paper-wrapped objects.

Setting: This play is written primarily for production on a bare stage with no scenery. It may, of course, be produced with the most elaborate stage effects, costumes, and mechanical devices.

Lighting: No special effects.

CATASTROPHE CLARENCE

Characters: 6 male.

Playing Time: 20 minutes.

Costumes: Everyday modern dress for Bob and Andy. The Professor and Glenn Matthews may wear lab coats over everyday modern suits. Howard wears horn-rimmed glasses, a chef's hat and apron. Catastrophe Clarence wears a fan-

232

tastic costume suitable to a space man.

Properties: Dusty jar with top, two suitcases, for Bob and Andy; notebook and pencil for Glenn Matthews; assortment of sacks, cartons, milk, salt, carton of eggs, box of corn flakes, two or three hot dogs, and other edibles.

Setting: Professor Clark's observatory in the San Bernardino Mountains. A large telescope stands at downstage left. At stage center, a table strewn with papers, and a comfortable armchair beside it. A file cabinet, one or two metal stools, and important-looking paraphernalia are scattered around the stage. There is an exit at left, leading outside, and an exit at right, leading to other rooms in the house. There is a window at upstage center, through which Clarence enters.

Lighting: If possible, the stage should brighten gradually as the meteor approaches, and darken again as the meteor recedes.

JOHN CROWN'S LEGACY

Characters: 26 male.
Playing Time: 30 minutes.
Costumes: John Citizen and John Crown wear suits. The rest of the characters wear costumes as suggested in the text, or costumes typical of the periods in which they lived and the work they did.
Properties: A projector and the various pictures indicated in the text, wheelchair for John Crown, quill pen for John Hancock, money bag for Robert Morris, spool and crank for Eli Whitney, blue-backed book for Noah Webster, sextant or spy glass for Nat Bowditch, ship model for

Donald McKay, bag of seeds for Johnny Appleseed, syringe for Dr. Morton, plant and grafting knife for Luther Burbank, blueprints for George Goethals, box containing a toy telegraph key, a bulb, a toy phonograph and a toy motion picture projector for Thomas Edison, wrench for Henry Ford.

Setting: This production may be staged simply or elaborately. The stage may be draped with bunting or left bare. Music may be supplied by an orchestra and glee club, or by a phonograph. Additional music may be added, to be used as a background or presented separately.

Lighting: No special effects.

YELLOW FEVER

Characters: 12 male.
Playing Time: 30 minutes.
Costumes: Gallagher wears white seersucker civilian clothes, with white tropical hat. Jansen wears white trousers and a white intern's tunic with high neck and buttons down the side. All others wear regulation khaki Army uniforms, Rough Rider style, with hats and insignia indicating rank.
Properties: Two desks; army cot; cabinet with glass doors; wooden table; books, pamphlets and papers; envelope with letter; flasks, test tubes, slides, microscope and miscellaneous laboratory equipment to give set authentic flavor; camp chairs or stools; palmleaf fan; watch; notebook and pencils; wire-mesh cage; magnifying glass; scalpel; desk lamps.
Setting: Simple interior set, with screened triple windows and door in rear wall. Windows can be

painted on set. If no scenery is available, a plain white cyclorama may be used effectively, with lighting concentrated in center of stage. Taut strips of cheesecloth can be substituted for screening on windows and doors.

Lighting: Scenes 1 and 3: Bright morning light; fully illuminated stage. Scenes 2 and 4: Night: dim lights, lighted desk lamps.

JIMINY CINDERS

Characters: 8 male.

Playing Time: 25 minutes.

Costumes: All characters at outset of play wear cowboy costumes, except Jiminy who wears blue jeans. Golden Ranger wears a gold-colored cowboy outfit—hat, vest, bandanna, trousers, boots, belt, lariat with six gold-colored holsters. His hat should be very large. Cowboy outfit for Jiminy including boots. Sheriff and Deputies also wear western outfits with jackets, and star-shaped badges.

Setting: The bunkhouse is a simple, crudely furnished room, with either two double bunks, or four small cots. Jiminy's cot should be separate from the others, and is loosely covered with a blanket. There is a table center with a few chairs around it. A water bucket and tin dipper are on stool, left. A fireplace on right wall, with logs in it, and a wood box next to it.

Properties: Broom; hat, boots, and belt for Jiminy; paper bag, handcuffs, box containing Golden Spurs; papers representing deed, etc.; golden lariat with gold whistle.

Lighting: No special effects.

ROBIN HOOD IN SHERWOOD FOREST

Characters: 13 male, plus any convenient number of males to play the outlaws.

Playing Time: 30 minutes.

Costumes: Percy and Egbert should be well dressed in the clothes of the period. Robin and his outlaws wear much hardier, plainer clothing of Lincoln green. David should wear shabby peasant dress; Friar Tuck must have a friar's gown; and Odlin, a soldier's garb.

Properties: Quarterstaves for Egbert and Percy; black-handled knife and sheath for Little Hubberd; friar's robe for Little John.

Setting: A glade in Sherwood Forest. The backdrop represents a forest. Before it is a row of high bushes. From the row of bushes, moving downstage on both left and right, are three tree wings on either side. In the very center of the stage is a large log. Downstage left center is a small log.

Lighting: No special effects.

THE FIRST CAT ON MARS

Characters: 9 male.

Playing Time: 25 minutes.

Costumes: All of the characters should wear khaki pants, khaki or white shirts (open at the neck, sleeves rolled up), and, if desired, officers' caps with visors. Insignias may be worn on the shirts; the Skipper's collar may have stars or bars on it.

Properties: Books, magazines, stuffed cat, crayon, ball of twine, papers, bottles, blankets, hotwater bottle, first-aid kits, sun lamp, crutches.

Setting: The control room of a Mars-bound rocket ship. The control panel with dials and knobs is across the left corner; its two "wings" with "radar" screen and switches run along the upper and side flats. The porthole is on the upstage wall; "stars" may be seen through it. A microphone is near the panel. A bulkhead door opens inward at right. The hull is represented by strips with rivets along them (paper streamers with silver disks attached) radiating from the panel, on the flats. Up right are two folding chairs with several magazines on them. There is a stool for the pilot at the panel. The calendar is to the side of the porthole.

Sound Effects: Employing a "live" microphone and speaker, backstage, the various sounds necessary to take-off and later scenes can be had from such things as a vacuum cleaner, roller skates, chains, whistles, and small electric motors.

Lighting: Lights should flicker during the meteor attack. If possible, there should be colored lights on the control panel that can flicker during the attack.

Most Memorable Voyage

Characters: 10 male; male extras.
Playing Time: 30 minutes.
Costumes: Hot-weather dress for 15th century mariners. Sailors with bare feet, brilliant silk scarves tied around their heads, shirts with necks open—perhaps one with no shirt. Loose thin trousers. Perhaps large gold earrings. Columbus and other "gentlemen" wear finer clothes, stockings and slippers, but even so, they are informal. Columbus' ruff around his neck is, for instance, open at the throat.

Properties: A small telescope, a writing portfolio, quill pen, ink well, rolled sheet of stiff paper (as for a map), bunch of seaweed, a small branched twig, a small smooth stick.

Setting: A section of the deck of 15th century sailing vessel. Deck railing runs all across rear of stage. A few feet back of this (to give a sense of distance) is the backdrop of sky and sea, with the low straight horizon line. Throughout the play, stage hands may manipulate the backdrop rhythmically raising and lowering each end a few inches—sometimes more, sometimes less—very slowly, to give the illusion of the ship's motion, except for a passage where a calm is designated.

On the stage are two wooden seachests, two buckets (preferably wooden ones) standing upside-down, and a pile of coiled rope. On the chests should appear the painted name of the ship, *Santa Maria*. Since the ship is moving from east to west, therefore from stage left to right, the audience becomes aware of this, as the actors in looking *ahead* for land, look toward the stage right wing. Offstage voices from the ship *Pinta* come from offstage right. Voices from the ship *Nina* come from offstage left.

Lighting: A darkened stage for the night scene, with a blue light overhead to depict moonlight. Red and yellow lights shining from right wing to depict sunset. (If necessary, special lighting effects may be omitted.)

Top of the Bill

Characters: 5 male.
Playing Time: 25 minutes.

Costumes: Pitter and Patter wear clown suits, hats, false noses and make-up when they first enter. Later they have on old clothes. Mr. Mashette wears evening dress and a top hat and carries a riding whip. Bobby and Frank wear everyday pants and sweaters or jackets.

Properties: String, two bicycles, sticks of red and white grease paint, box, bags, plates, bag of flour, saucepan, towels.

Setting: A clearing near the Big Top. Upstage right is the side of a caravan; this should have a few steps leading up to a door, and large windows on either side of the door. Upstage center, in front of some bushes, is a table with a bench behind it. On the table are two mirrors, make-up boxes, towels, plates, a saucepan, a small bag of flour and other cooking utensils. A log is lying downstage left. The entrance at left leads to the Big Top, the one at right, to the road.

Lighting: No special effects.

THE CRYING CLOWN

Characters: 4 male.

Playing Time: 10 minutes.

Costumes: The Clown is dressed in a gaudy clown suit and oversized shoes. He wears typical make-up. The Circus Owner wears a business suit with a carnation in his buttonhole. He carries a bowler hat and cane. The Cop wears a typical uniform and carries a billy club. The Boy is dressed in everyday clothes.

Properties: Large hanky with a hole in the middle of it, two regular hankies, large red hanky on which is written in white letters, "The End."

Setting: The area just outside a circus tent. If possible, the tent should form part of the backdrop so that the Boy can wiggle under it in making his entrance. A bench is the only essential piece of furniture.

Lighting: No special effects.

KING JOHN AND THE ABBOT OF CANTERBURY

Characters: 7 male; may be additional court attendants for Scene 4.

Playing Time: 20 minutes.

Costumes: Shepherd is dressed in close-fitting brown trousers fastened to the knee with hempen cord; tan tunic; long brown hooded cloak. King John wears tunic of gold cloth, crimson hose, a long crimson cape, and a gold crown. The First Nobleman wears a tunic of figured brocade, a short green cape, green hose. He carries a sword at his side. The Second Nobleman wears a silver tunic, tan velvet cape, tan hose, and carries a sword at his side. The Abbot has a beard and wears purple robes trimmed with white fur. The Regents wear black velvet robes over their gowns of different shades—one light blue and one yellow.

Properties: A heavy walking stick representing shepherd's crook.

Setting: For Scene 1, there is a tall hedge across the rear with low bushes along the side, to give effect of country roadside. Scene 2 may be made to look lavish with large throne decorated with gold (gold paint may be used), and draped with dark purple velvet or anything else to suggest sumptuous furnishings. Scene 3 requires only a table and a few

chairs. Scene 4 is the same as
Scene 2.
Lighting: No special effects.

THE RUNAWAY PIRATE

Characters: 4 male; male extras.
Playing Time: 10 minutes.
Costumes: The Pirate wears the
traditional pirate costume, with
bandanna, ear rings, colored
blouse, black full knickers and
black boots. The other characters
may be completely uniformed, or
can wear special hats; the pilot, a
helmet and goggles, the officer
and captain, caps with visors,
the sailors, white sailors' caps.
Properties: Cutlass, black pirate flag
with skull and cross bones, spy
glass.
Setting: A harbor. The backdrop
should be painted to look like an
ocean. Around the stage are
benches, kegs, boxes, and other
equipment like fishing nets, etc.
Sound Effects: Boat whistle, roar of
airplane motor.
Lighting: No special effects.

HOME, SWEET HOME

Characters: 6 male; male extras.
Playing Time: 10 minutes.
Costumes: Peek and Tiptoe wear
grey clothes and have mouse ears
and tails. Other characters all
wear appropriately colored clothes
and possibly masks, representing
the various animals. Rabbit
should wear big white ears.
Properties: Red kerchiefs, sticks,
twigs, board, two chairs.

Setting: A barnyard, with a big
red barn at one corner of the
stage, and a corn crib at one
side of it. Two chairs tipped over
can represent Rabbit's hole at
the other side of the stage.
Lighting: No special effects.

THE FORTUNE OF MERRYLEGS AND
TAWNY-WHISKERS

Characters: 11 male.
Playing Time: 20 minutes.
Costumes: Merrylegs wears a belted
tunic of green with long green
cotton hose and dark slippers.
Tawny-Whiskers (played by a
small child) may wear an outfit
made of black material with very
noticeable yellow "whiskers." The
Baker wears a white cap and
apron over his trousers and shirt.
His Apprentices are dressed the
same. The Brew Master wears a
short, brown tunic. His Serving
Men wear tan tunics. The Schoolmaster wears a blue tunic and a
long dark blue cape and a broad-
brimmed hat.
Properties: Piece of silver; a bell;
huge beating spoon; a large tray
filled with long, flat loaves of
bread and another tray filled
with sweet rolls and tarts; small
barrel; walking staff and large
book for Schoolmaster.
Setting: A room in an old inn.
There are a simple table and some
chairs about the room. There
is a blackened fireplace with
an iron pot on the crane. A
bench stands to the left of the
fireplace.
Lighting: No special effects.